BOUDICCA

WHO WAS...

BOUDICCA

Warrior Queen

SIÂN BUSBY

Illustrations by Alex Fox

✴ SHORT BOOKS

First published in 2006 by
Short Books
15 Highbury Terrace
London N5 1UP

10 9 8 7 6 5 4 3 2 1

A CIP catalogue record for this book
is available from the British Library.

Illustration copyright © Alex Fox 2006
Quiz by Sebastian Blake

ISBN 1-904977-60-X

Printed in Great Britain by
Bookmarque Ltd., Croydon, Surrey

For my nieces and nephews: Laura, Charlotte, Eve, Michael,
Fraser, Eleanor, Frances, Reece, Thomas and Mairi;
and my sons, Simon and Max
(with special thanks to Max for all his help)

Be Proud!

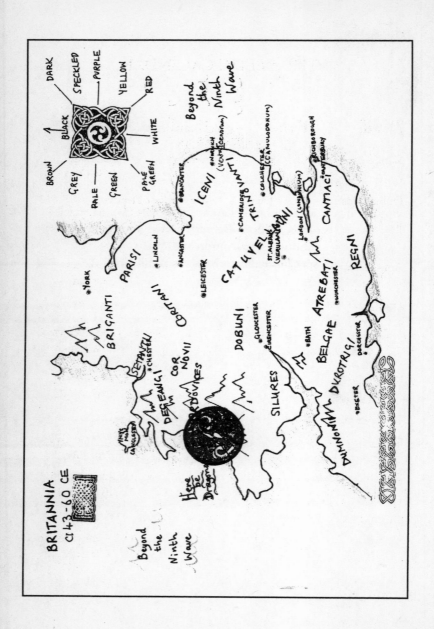

THE CELTIC CALENDAR

Month	Period	Meaning	Festival
Samonios	Oct / Nov	Seed-fall	Samhain, 31st Oct
Dumannios	Nov / Dec	The Darkest Depths	
Riuros	Dec / Jan	Cold-time	Winter Solstice, 21 Dec
Anagantios	Jan / Feb	Stay-home-time	Oimelc, 31st Jan
Ogronios	Feb / Mar	Time of Ice	
Cutios	Mar / Apr	Time of Winds	Spring Equinox, 21st March
Giamonios	Apr / May	Shoots-show	Beltane 30th April
Simivisionios	May / Jun	Time of Brightness	
Equos	Jun / Jul	Horse-time	Summer Solstice 21st June
Elembiuos	Jul / Aug	Claim-time	Lughnasadh 31st July
Edrinios	Aug / Sep	Arbitration-time	
Cantios	Sep / Oct	Song-time	Autumn Equinox 21st Sept

PROLOGUE
The Time of Brightness
North Wales; May, 140CE

"Don't be stupid! A girl can't be a hunter!" jeered Cadman the fighter at his big sister, who stood in the yard throwing seed to the hens. Their father had just announced that he would take the annoying brat hunting for the first time the next day, and Cadman was swaggering about the yard like a mighty warrior just home from a successful raid.

"But father promised he'd take *me* next time," cried Gwendoline, she of the white brow, and the tallest by far of all the girls in the village. "Why should you get to go? You're two years younger than I am!"

"Girls are supposed to stay at home with their mothers and spin yarn," scorned her brother. "They aren't strong enough to throw spears, or shoot an arrow at a deer! Girls bake bread while they're waiting for the men to come home hungry from the forest!"

Gwendoline burned scarlet and threw the basket of seed onto the ground. The chickens clucked and gobbled at her feet.

"Hey you!" she yelled at Cadman, as he stuck his tongue out at her. "In the olden times the women of our people were governed by a great Warrior Queen," she said, tossing her long, red hair.

"Ugh," sneered Cadman, "she must have been very ugly! Just like you!"

Gwendoline felt anger surge through her veins. "She led a great army into battle with her chariot! And I'm going to be just like her!"

"Liar! Liar!" jeered Cadman.

Gwendoline saw red; she threw herself at Cadman and grappled him to the ground. The chickens squawked as the two of them wrestled in the dust of the yard. Being bigger and stronger, Gwendoline soon had the better of Cadman, who was thrashing his arms and legs about uselessly.

"Gwendoline! Gwendoline! Stop that at once!" The sound of her mother coming from the door of the villa stopped the girl just in time. "Get up off the ground, you wicked child!"

Gwendoline was in disgrace, and not for the first time. She stood up reluctantly.

"I sent you out here to feed the chickens," her mother

was saying, "not fight your little brother!"

"But it's not fair!" howled Gwendoline, her grey eyes like a stormy sea. "He called me a liar! He said girls can't be queens and warriors."

Her mother held up her hand to halt the flow of protestations. "I'm not interested in hearing your excuses," she declared. "It appears that Grandmother has filled your head with all sorts of nonsense about the past," mother continued coldly. "It would have been better if she had taught you about the great men of your family; your father was a Primus Pilus, in charge of an elite cohort of Roman soldiers. And your grandfather supervised the building of the great white road."

From behind their mother's skirts Cadman was pulling faces at Gwendoline. She felt her temper rise up again.

"You are not," her mother continued, "some common fishwife who brawls in the market-place. As a punishment you will go and clean out the pigsty. Perhaps then you will learn not to be so proud and ill-tempered."

Gwendoline felt such a strong sense of injustice that she almost sat down on the ground and cried. But, she told herself, that was not the sort of thing a warrior queen would do. Gwendoline was not sure what a warrior queen would do instead, but she knew someone who would know for sure.

Gwendoline was still fuming when she arrived at the tiny, old-fashioned roundhouse where her mother's mother's mother dwelt. It was on the very edge of the village, close by where the great white road leads over the hills to the next village and beyond. She found the frail old woman in the dark of the thatched building, stooped over her cauldron, where a thick cawl bubbled and filled the little dwelling with a delicious aroma. Through the heat haze of the cauldron the old woman seemed to be shimmering like an apparition. She was leaning upon a crooked hazel stick, and her fingers, as they clasped it, looked like long, spindly twigs.

"I know you," she said, peering through the smoke. The girl jumped and swallowed hard, trying not to look scared. "I know you by your grey eyes and your high, white forehead," continued the old woman. "I know you by your bold expression." It was plain to anyone looking from Gwendoline to the old woman that they were each made of the same noble blood and fine bones, and they had the same pale skin and rich auburn hair.

"What are you afraid of, child?" the old woman asked sternly.

"Nothing," declared Gwendoline stoutly. "I'm not afraid of anything."

"You must be frightened of something," she said at last, "or you would not be so angry." Gwendoline frowned, puzzled. "Well then, let us start the other way around," said great-grandmother. "Tell me, child, what are you so angry about?"

"My brother said I was a liar, and that girls can't be warriors and so I fought him, and mother said I had to clean out the pigsty, and it's not fair, so I've run away and I want you to tell me how I can be a great warrior queen when I grow up," said Gwendoline.

"I see," said the old woman thoughtfully. "Well, I can tell that you are afraid of a good many things."

"No I'm not!" said Gwendoline tossing her hair.

"Firstly," her great-grandmother continued, "you are afraid that your parents love your brother more than you; secondly you are afraid that nobody will believe you even when you speak a great truth; thirdly, you are afraid that, because you are a girl, you are doomed to a boring life of feeding chickens, instead of the one filled with the adventure you so desire. Well, these are certainly very big fears."

Gwendoline stopped sulking, and blinked in silent astonishment. She was surprised to hear all of this, and had to admit it was all true. "How did you know?" she began, feeling a tingle of fear creep up her spine.

The old woman nodded slowly to herself. "Well, now, come child. See that bowl of mixture on the floor there by the hearth? Why don't you sit on the floor beside the fire and make some little cakes for me? Take pinches of dough and squash them flat in between your palms, and place the little discs upon the bakestone set in the fire there. And while you are doing that I will tell you all about the warrior queen. It is our sacred duty to learn from the past, after all.

And I am a Bard. It is through me that the stories of the past must live on into the future."

Gwendoline was feeling a little afraid, but her desire to hear the story of the Warrior Queen was also very strong. And so she did as she was bid, and her great-grandmother settled herself on a stool beside the cauldron.

"I shall tell you about the ancient days of our people," she said in her story-telling voice, which was more singing than speaking. "A time long ago many of the tribes from these islands – which had for so long warred against each other – joined together under one mighty queen to fight the Strangers."

"What did she look like?" asked the girl.

"She was magnificent," answered the old woman, "tall and strong-boned, with thick red hair. Her eyes were grey and sharp as flint. That day of all days she seemed invincible as she stood on the battlefield, her roar urging her army on."

As she placed the first of the little cakes on to the bake-stone, Gwendoline tried to picture the beautiful Queen.

"But," said the old Bard, her voice dropping ominously, "to the Strangers waiting to do battle on the far side of the plain she was no valiant goddess of war. To them she was a screeching, blood-caked demon. Imagine her in a mighty chariot: horses galloping towards you; the blood-stained blades fixed to the hub of the great wheels, turning, hacking through everything and everyone that stood in their path."

Gwendoline felt her heart pounding at the thought of this fearless woman, galloping towards her through the mists of time.

"That morning," continued the old woman, "the Roman centurions mocked the men under their command, trying to shame them into courage. 'What? Are you afraid of a mere woman?' they laughed. 'Legionaries, stand firm, stand firm!' And then a hush fell upon the ranks, as the Legate Suetonius Paulinus himself addressed them. He swept his arm in the direction of the Queen's army ranged on the plain below. 'Look at them,' he sneered. 'Nobody steeped in the discipline and order of the Imperial Legions could possibly call that an army.'

"'Look at them,' the Legate commanded his men, 'and ask yourselves, what is there to fear? Look and you will see there are more women than warriors.' The legionaries swallowed hard and looked upon their foe, whose half-naked and painted bodies were contorted into wild dances."

"So the Romans were afraid of the Queen? Even though she was a woman?" asked Gwendoline, hugging her knees tightly.

The Old Bard nodded slowly. "Oh yes, the Strangers were very afraid of the Queen, and with good reason. But the Legate was a powerful commander. 'They are not worthy to be our enemy, they are our slaves!'

He told his cohorts: "The Britons will surrender the moment they see your javelins raining down upon them.

Remember that you are Romans, and that together we have conquered half the globe with our courage, whereas the Britons are lawless savages, little better then beasts."

"The the men of the XIVth and XXth Legions tried not to think of dying. Instead, they thought of their mothers back home; of the balmy air and lemon trees of Amalfi; of the deep blue of the Mediterranean gently lapping golden sands. They muttered prayers under their breath, asking their gods that this might not be their last day on earth.

"Imagine what they thought," her great-grandmother continued, "in the moments before the command to charge, those terrified Romans. They tried not to think of the gibbet, the stake, the fire and the sword; the human sacrifices made to strange gods: their brother legionaries impaled, roasted alive like oxen, boiled like pigs' heads."

"Yuck!" cried Gwendoline. Her father was a Roman, and she didn't like to think of him being barbecued.

"Well, that was the way back then, you see," said her great-grandmother matter-of-factly. "The Strangers feared those ancient customs more than anything – well, almost anything." The Bard lifted her old head, noble and proud. "What they feared most was waiting for them out there on the plain; standing aloft in her blood-stained chariot, the one we called Queen Boudicca."

"Queen Boudicca!" whispered Gwendoline.

The old woman smiled strangely at the girl. "It was said that there were seven sights in her eyes, and that she had the power to be all around you and everywhere at once, like a mountain mist."

Gwendoline was completely transfixed by the idea of a queen so formidable that even the Romans were afraid of her. "She must have been fantastic!" she breathed, staring deep into the flames licking around the base of the cauldron. "And did she win?" she asked, her pale skin flushed with excitement. "Oh, great-grandmother, tell me, tell me: did she win the battle?"

The old woman smiled. "Child, child!" she said. "Let me tell you the whole story, and when I am done, if you are as clever as I think, perhaps you will find the answer to your own question." And settling back on the little stool, the hazel stick clasped firm in her bony hands, the Bard closed her eyes, and in her sing-song, story-telling voice she began.

CHAPTER 1
Shoots-show
Beltane, 30th April, 43CE

❝ My tale begins on the Feast of Beltane almost one hundred years ago: the night the Strangers came and everything changed for ever.

It wasn't their first visit. The Strangers had visited our lands almost one hundred years before. That time they took a good look around, fought a few battles, burned down a few villages, stole a load of silver and gold, and then went back to their own lands. Of course they took some of our people with them as slaves. Oh yes, and before they left they warned our great-grandparents that they'd be back, only with an even bigger army, unless – that is, we paid tributes to their King, the one they called the Caesar.

Over the years there was a great deal of grumbling about the tributes paid to the Caesar; but everybody paid them all the same. And, as long as they did, the Strangers kept to their part of the bargain: they didn't come back… until that summer's eve long ago.

Back in those days our people lived in a place called Icenia which lay in the Yellow Lands, far away across the mountains, on the edge of the other great sea.

Not one, but two mighty Chieftains ruled over Icenia: their names were Antedios and Prasutagus, and there never were two men more unlike one another. Antedios was very shrewd and cunning, but he was not all that good at fighting. Prasutagus, on the other hand, was much too blunt and straightforward to be good at sneaky plots, but he was the bravest and most feared warrior in the whole region.

In his youth, Prasutagus led countless raids on the lands bordering Icenia, earning a fearsome reputation for his courage and ruthlessness, and for many years, the mere mention of his name was enough to strike terror into the hearts of even the bravest rival chieftain. The young Prasutagus, you see, cut down champions as if they were rushes, laughing as he did so; he never left a battlefield until it was soaked in blood. He kept the heads for himself, tying them to his horse's harness.

On the good side, Prasutagus brought back a lot of stuff from these raids: not just heads, but cattle, slaves, gold torcs and all sorts of other precious things; all of which helped to make the Iceni the wealthiest and most powerful tribe in all the Yellow Lands.

Now, a lot of people thought that Prasutagus was so

brave and tough that he ought to be King of the whole tribe; but there were others who thought that brains were more important than brawn in a King, and they argued that Antedios would be a better choice. For years the argument went on, with everyone taking one side or another. Prasutagus and his side were always challenging Antedios to ferocious battles, and Antedios and his side were always plotting against Prasutagus. This long and bloody quarrel left scores of the bravest Iceni warriors either horribly mutilated, or dead.

The rest of the tribe began to fear that soon there would be no warriors left in Icenia to defend the lands, and this concern became especially important when the tricky Catuvellauni, who occupied the White Lands, produced a warrior every bit as fearless as the young Prasutagus had been. He was called Caradoc.

Caradoc's Catuvellauni had all but destroyed the Iceni's nearest neighbours, the Trinovanti, before going on to attack the Atrebati. It was quite easy for Caradoc to take over the whole place.

With such a dangerous lunatic breathing down their necks, it was obvious that the Iceni would have to do something to end the in-fighting between Prasutagus and Antedios. The Druids decided the best thing would be to summon Prasutagus and Antedios to a tribal council, where each of them could put forward his case as to why he ought to be the King of Icenia.

The debate raged for hour upon hour without reaching any agreement. It would have been better for everyone if one of the chieftains had had just a little of the skill the other possessed: if Prasutagus had possessed a modicum of cunning; or Antedios a scintilla of courage. Unfortunately, that was not the case: Prasutagus was quite simply not all that clever, and Antedios was such a coward that he had trained his only child, a daughter, to fight his battles for him.

After a long time discussing the matter a wise old Druid finally came up with a suggestion. Surely, he reasoned, the best thing for the whole tribe would be if the two mighty Lords were to share the task of being King between them. If they could manage to combine their different skills and work together in harmony, then perhaps the Iceni would become the most powerful tribe in the whole of the Yellow Lands.

Everyone agreed that this was the best plan, but now the problem was how to persuade Prasutagus and Antedios that this sensible solution was in their best interest too? The Druids thought long and hard before one of them came up with a fiendishly clever solution.

Should one of the mighty princes ever take up arms, or plot against the other, he would suffer a four-fold death.

First of all he would suffer death by air: that is, the Druids would hang him from the highest branch of the mightiest oak in the forest until he was almost choked.

Secondly, he would suffer death by water: the Druids would tie his hands and feet together and throw him off a rock in to the great sea, where they would let him almost drown. Thirdly, he would suffer death by fire: the Druids would put the troublemaking King in a huge wicker-basket shaped like a man, to which they would then set fire, leaving him there until he almost burned. Finally, he would suffer death by earth: the Druids would tie him up and lay him face down in the marshes until his lungs filled up with mud and he stopped breathing altogether.

It was a brilliant scheme. And just to make it absolutely clear that they were serious, the Druids also decreed that the surviving King – even if he had done nothing wrong – would be bound hand and foot, placed in a fishing coracle and set afloat on the next receding tide.

Hearing this, Prasutagus and Antedios figured out very quickly that they would be better off reconciling their differences and agreeing to rule peaceably together. To seal the contract Prasutagus, who had spent so many years dashing about the place fighting that he had never found the time to settle down with the right woman, agreed to marry Antedios's daughter – a girl who had been brought up by her father to be as strong and bold as she was beautiful.

She went by the name of Boudicca.

For a couple of years, the Iceni prospered under the joint kingship of Prasutagus and Antedios, and life was good and happy. There was great wealth, certainly more than enough to pay the Strangers to stay away; and now that there was less fighting amongst themselves the tribes-people had more time to do other things, like looking after their land and herds.

Of course, there were still battles to fight: warrior chieftains from the neighbouring tribes were always keen to make a name for themselves by attempting to bring home the head of the mighty Prasutagus. Greedy rival Kings wanted to get their hands on all that Iceni gold and their cows and slaves.

And, of course, there was always Prince Caradoc, out on the misty borders, waiting for a chance to sneak in and declare himself King of Icenia. Everyone in the whole region was sick and tired of Caradoc and his unruly ways. And the really worrying thing was that he was now going around declaring that he had absolutely no intention of paying the tributes owed to the Caesar out of the stuff he had stolen from the Atrebati and the Trinovanti. Absolutely no way! It was his stuff now, he said. If the Caesar wants it, he can come and get it. He knows where I am.

"Caradoc is an idiot!" said Antedios when he heard this.

Prasutagus was surprised. Up until now, he had been thinking that Caradoc sounded like a pretty fine fellow to him. "What do you mean?" he asked.

Antedios narrowed his eyes, which always made Prasutagus feel uneasy. "What do you think is going to happen when the Caesar finds out that the tributes from the

Atrebati and Trinovanti are not as big as they should be?" Antedios asked.

And so that was how things stood in Icenia, on that particular Feast of Beltane, the night the Strangers arrived and nothing was ever the same again.

***

That night a great host of Iceni people had gathered at Prasutagus's hill-fort to celebrate the triumph of the sun-god over the powers of darkness. In the enclosure outside the great hall, the Druids had built the sacred bonfires and they were standing by, ready to light them by catching the first ray of summer light sent from the flames of the sun-god himself as he rode across the sky.

Everyone had brought their cattle out of the winter stalls to have them blessed. They were excited as they eagerly awaited the dawn; dancing and singing; listening to the tales told by the finest Bards in the land; gorging on a huge feast of roast oxen and hog meat, and guzzling sweet ale and cakes.

As soon as darkness fled from the sky, the young men and women of the Iceni would be joining hands to dance around the sacred bonfires; the cattle would be driven through the middle of the flames, and every man, woman and child of the tribe would call upon the sun-god to protect the herd from evil, just as the Iceni had done every

Beltane since the very first dawn.

In those days the wealth of a tribe was measured by the size of its cattle herd, and that Beltane, as the beasts lumbered out of their stalls, blinking at the sunlight, it was plain to everyone that the Iceni were rich beyond imagining.

Well, all of this would have been cause enough for celebration, but just a few days before the feast Prasutagus's wife, Queen Boudicca, the daughter of King Antedios, had given birth to her first child.

It was a healthy baby girl and she was to be called Briana, the strong. While the whole fort was thronging with joyful Iceni, in the relative calm and quiet of the Royal bed chamber, the priestesses of the goddess Andraste were getting ready to divine a great future for the baby princess, who, it was believed, would one day rule over all of Icenia.

It caused a great shock, then, when news came that the Strangers had arrived in the night.

The dismal intelligence was brought by a young fisherman of the Trinovanti tribe: a boy of about twelve years old, whose name was Finian the Handsome. He had been caught attempting to wade through the marsh reeds that surrounded King Prasutagus's fort, and should really have been killed there and then, as was the custom in those days. But somehow Finian the Handsome managed to convince his captors that they should let him live. They dragged Finian into the feasting chamber and threw him at the feet of the mighty Prasutagus.

The warriors had been toasting all day and by now were very drunk; their spirits were high, their tempers hot; they had reached the stage of the feast where they all took it in turns to boast of their battle prowess and feats of strength, and that nearly always led to arguments.

Imagine how poor Finian's heart must have raced inside his chest when he found himself surrounded by a host of warriors, all preparing to draw their knives against him.

Luckily for the young fisherman, Prasutagus himself was in a particularly good mood. He had been entertaining all day long, and the Iceni chieftains had brought him lots of gifts: cows, sheep, goats, horses, precious stones and decorations, iron, bronze, silver and gold, piles of food and gallons of drink. He was happy that he had such a beautiful wife and a bonny baby daughter. He was looking forward to summer and long days spent hunting and fishing.

Prasutagus waved his champions aside with the pig hock he was eating and beckoned Finian to come forward.

"What business do you have here?" he commanded.

Little Finian was trembling from head to foot as he knelt in front of the King. "Mighty Lord," he said, his voice quivering, "I sped here as fast as the mist coming in from the sea. My feet hardly touched the earth. I did not bother with tracks, but followed the shortest route across the marsh reed beds…"

"Yes, yes," interrupted Prasutagus, "I want to know why you have come here, not how…" At this the Icenian chieftains roared with laughter, and poor Finian, who was actually not all that keen on being a fisherman at all and rather fancied himself as a Bard, looked about him nervously. King Prasutagus did not join in the mirth; he settled back in his great throne, his eyes locked on the young boy.

Prasutagus was growing old; his noble head was crowned by tufts of white hair stiffened with lime, and two long white moustaches hung down either side of his mouth. But his body was hard as granite and his muscles bulged in tight knots beneath his tattooed skin.

"I can see," said Prasutagus peering hard at the boy, "that what stands before me is not of the warrior class; in fact," and here the King sniffed the air, "I can tell that you are nothing more, nor less, than a fisherman."

"Yes, yes, great King," grovelled Finian, "you are as wise as you are mighty…"

"You talk too much," said Prasutagus bluntly. "Have you ever thought of being a Bard? Still," he continued leaning forward to look deep into Finian's eyes, "you meet my gaze with a certain fierce pride, which is not all born of fear."

When at last Prasutagus motioned the boy to continue with his tale the poor wretch almost dropped to the floor with relief, his words tumbling out like a haul of fish tipped on to a jetty. One by one the Iceni chieftains put down their horn flasks and turned to listen to his tale.

"Mighty King, I bring you word that Strangers have come into the Red Lands. I saw them with my own eyes when I was laying out my nets. They were wading ashore at the mouth of the great river which divides our land from that of the Cantiaci."

"Strangers, eh?" mused the King stroking his moustaches. "How many, would you say, of these… Strangers?"

"Oh, mighty Lord, they are beyond number." Sensing that everyone in the hall was now listening to him, Finian, who loved to perform, began to warm to his mission. "They have come war-shouldered. I saw their metal heads glinting in the light of the moon, like so many herrings in an eddy. They carried vast banners which rippled in the breeze, as long and broad as a stream, and smooth and shining as polished pebbles."

Prasutagus leant forward, grabbing the fisherman by the

shoulders and thrusting his face in close. He spoke very soft-ly: "Do you lie to me?"

"N-n-no great Lord, m-m-mighty K-K-King."

"Is this some trick? The truth now...."

"B-b-by the g-g-gods that my p-p-people s-s-swear by, I saw their m-m-metal heads... I ran here as f-f-fast as I c-c-could."

A few weak beams of moonlight were penetrating the cracks in the thatched walls of the smoky hall. In the half-light Finian could just make out the severed heads of Prasutagus's enemies, preserved in cedar oil and arranged on the wall behind the King. Their eyes were open wide in anguish, their mouths gaping.

The young fisherman gathered his wits. He pulled him-self up to his full height and swallowed his fear in a gulp.

"It's the truth, my Lord," he said with a renewed bold-ness, "everything I have said is the truth. There are Strangers in the Red Lands. You may kill me if you wish: I have no fear of death, but killing me will not stop the Strangers from coming to Icenia." It was such a fine speech, that Prasutagus released his grip on the young fisherman.

"Give this lad food and drink," he ordered his atten-dants. "You know," he continued, smiling approvingly at Finian, "you have quite a way with words." And that was how Finian the handsome became a Bard to King Prasutagus.

The King then summoned two of his bravest champions.

"Go into the woods and wilds beyond our lands here," he commanded them, "and tell me what goes on. Do not return until you have proof of the dangers that lurk across our misty plains."

***

"May her arms be as white and long as a swan's neck, their tops as smooth as snow on a hill-brow; may her hair be the colour of polished gold; may she be as savage as the she-wolf in the protection of her brood; may she be as shrill as the owl shattering the night sky with her warning..." The Priestess stopped her chant over the head of Boudicca's baby daughter and looked across to the chamber entrance, where King Prasutagus stood deep in thought.

Boudicca laid Briana gently in the crib. Motioning to the Priestess to leave, she crossed to her husband and slipped her arms about his neck.

"My love," he whispered to the beautiful young woman, his queen. In the torchlight her eyes blazed like a sword. They could, he knew, pierce all the secrets of his soul.

"What is it Prasutagus?" she commanded, pulling away from him. "Something's wrong, I can tell."

Prasutagus stroked his long white moustaches and sighed deeply, wondering how best he might tell his queen about the arrival of the Strangers. He knew that their presence in the Red Lands was sure to lead to trouble, and it was the thought of all that trouble which was making his head ache and his heart heavy.

Never forget that in his youth Prasutagus had been the most bloodthirsty warrior in all of the Yellow Lands. But in the past couple of years, ever since he had stopped fighting with Antedios and settled down with Boudicca, he had begun to change.

He had begun to see that there was more to life than killing people. He had discovered a fondness for music and Bardic verses – especially those which told of how great he was. He liked just spending time in the hill-fort with his friends and family; or going for long rides across Icenia; hunting, fishing. Most of all, he loved spending time with his beautiful wife Boudicca: the only woman strong enough to steal his heart.

"Well," he would tell himself on waking every morning, "I never expected to live this long: I always imagined I would die in a fierce battle, and yet, here I am, still alive; and a mighty King as well. And here lying beside me is the boldest and most beautiful woman in the whole world!"

Boudicca had been a little difficult at first, and it had taken Prasutagus some time to accustom himself to life with someone who was always so sure of what she thought and felt. She had certainly made it quite clear to her father, Antedios, when he had broken the news of her marriage to her.

"But I don't want to get married," she had thundered.

She had stomped about the place, smashing things and hitting people and made such a terrible fuss that even her slave and best friend Cara could not placate her. "I don't want to spend the rest of my life looking after some stupid man," Boudicca roared, "I am destined to be a great queen!"

Of course, Antedios had nobody but himself to blame for the terrible tantrum his daughter was throwing. Boudicca's mother had died when she was very young, and Antedios had never married again. Boudicca was his only child and, as he was so bad at fighting himself, he had seen to it that she was taught all the skills that a warrior needed to know, by some of Icenia's best champions. In this way, Antedios hoped to ensure that Boudicca would be tough enough to be Queen of all Icenia when he died. Unfortunately, he hadn't reckoned with Boudicca being so big and strong and good at fighting – it was soon almost impossible for him to control his own daughter.

"Boudicca," he implored, "if you don't marry Prasutagus, the Druids won't let me be King. And then you won't be Queen. Do you see, my love?"

But Boudicca was never all that susceptible to sweet-talk. "Why don't you let me fight Prasutagus for the throne?" she suggested, in deadly earnest. "At least then my honour and pride would be satisfied!"

Antedios groaned and explained about the Druids' horrible threat.

Boudicca fumed. She was absolutely disgusted with

Antedios for having sold her short, but on the other hand, he was her father and she loved him.

She also loved Icenia. "If the Druids think that this is really in the best interest of the whole tribe," she reasoned to herself, "I suppose that I ought to go along with it."

"Alright, I'll do it," she declared after thinking a long time, "I'll marry that great, stupid oaf, Prasutagus. But I won't stand for any nonsense from him. I just hope he knows what he's letting himself in for."

***

"I'm only marrying you for the sake of the Iceni, you know," Boudicca informed Prasutagus on their wedding day. "You needn't get any ideas in your head about romance or any of that soppy nonsense. I love Icenia with my entire heart, and there's no room left over for any man."

Prasutagus was amazed to hear a girl talk this way. "But, I love Icenia too," was all he could think to say.

"I like to ride my horse very fast across the plains," she continued, "I go swimming every day, no matter how cold it is, and I prefer hunting with a spear to using a cudgel. Oh, and by the way, I am a rotten cook, so don't expect to come home to a pile of freshly-baked flatcakes."

No doubt, a lot of men in his situation would have turned tail and run away, but not Prasutagus. He was delighted! He loved riding his horse fast across the plains too, he actually preferred swimming in freezing cold water, and he loved hunting with spears. It wasn't very long at all before he realised that he loved this bold girl with her glorious red hair.

It must be said, however, that it took a little while longer for Boudicca to feel the same way about Prasutagus. Not that this troubled him: for one of the most exciting things about her was that he was never quite sure what she felt for him. She could be so bossy and make him feel such an idiot; and then in another moment she would turn and smile at him and he would fall in love with her all over again.

She was smiling now, on that Beltane eve, as Prasutagus held her close in their chamber; and seeing her so happy, for a moment, he almost forgot all about his worrying news.

"The priestess says that Briana will be a mighty queen," she was telling him, her beautiful eyes shining brightly. "She will have the strength and courage of a lioness and will never bring shame upon her tribe!"

Prasutagus smiled adoringly, and stroked her hair. At first Boudicca had been very cross about being pregnant: she had stamped about the fort shouting at everyone, full of rage that she wouldn't be able to ride her horse until after the baby was born. But as she had got fatter and rounder it seemed to everyone that she also grew a little softer. For Prasutagus those days and nights they spent together, just the two of them, as they waited for their baby to arrive, were the happiest days of his whole life.

Oh, thought Prasutagus, why did the Strangers have to come now, just when everything was so good?

"Are you… Are you crying, Prasutagus?" demanded Boudicca, peering at him, her eyes stretched with astonishment. The King sniffed and rubbed his eyes.

"No, no. It's just a cinder," he said, "that's all. A piece of dust."

"Well," laughed Boudicca, "imagine! For a moment there I thought that you were crying! Ha! That would have been funny!"

"Yes," murmured Prasutagus. "Yes, that would have been very funny. Boudicca, my love," he sighed and then continued, tentatively, "I'm afraid that something's happened."

"Something bad?" said the Queen eagerly.

"Possibly," replied the King. "It's difficult to know for sure." He sighed heavily and crossed over to the crib and stood there looking down at the sleeping form of his tiny daughter. "Remember how your father worried about the Atrebati king bleating to the Caeser about Caradoc?"

"Yes," flashed Boudicca, "and remember how we all had a good laugh, imagining how the Caesar would send the snivelling hound straight back to Atrebates with his tail between his legs?"

"Boudicca, Boudicca," sighed Prasutagus, "will you please just listen for a moment?" She looked at him, astonished: Prasutagus very rarely told her to shut up. "Please, darling," he continued, "I dare say that the Caesar listened to his whining and snivelling with little more than a passing interest; but what if he told him that because Caradoc had stolen all their treasure the Atrebati could no longer pay their tributes to Rome? And that if the Caesar wanted these tributes he would have to come and get them himself from Caradoc?"

"I'd like to see the Caesar try that!" said Boudicca.

"This is serious," Prasutagus said sharply. "The deal our forefathers made with the Strangers was that we would render unto the Caesar what is his, otherwise there would be big trouble. And now, thanks to Caradoc and his wild ways, it seems that big trouble is what we're facing."

Prasutagus was never sure how Boudicca would respond to anything. To be honest, he had been a little concerned that, seeing as now she was a mother, she might actually be afraid to hear about the Strangers coming; she might be worried about Prasutagus having to go and fight them. He should have known better. It worried him to see a flush of excitement colouring her pale cheek.

"Boudicca," he said in a warning tone. "Remember that we have to agree any course of action with your father. We must only do what we think is best for Icenia."

Prasutagus was relieved to see that his queen appeared to be thinking. He was the first to say that she was much cleverer than he was, if only she could stop being so hot-headed.

"Well," she said after a few moments, "that stupid

big-head Caradoc has really landed himself in hot water this time. I mean, it's great, isn't it, that the Strangers have come here to see him off for us? After all, as my father will no doubt say, that's what we pay them for! Yes, why not continue to suck up to the Caesar, and pay our tributes like good boys and girls?"

At first Prasutagus was pleased to hear Boudicca talk such sense. But then it dawned on him that Boudicca was in fact being horribly sarcastic. "Well we have enough wealth to pay the tributes the Caesar demands from us, don't we?" he said defensively. "The system has worked perfectly well for a hundred years, hasn't it? Why go looking for trouble?"

Boudicca raised her eyebrows and fixed him with one of her more formidable looks. "It's all very well, as long as the Caesar stops at putting Caradoc in his place, and doesn't decide to use all this as an excuse to demand more money from the rest of us."

Prasutagus looked a little puzzled. "Oh, he wouldn't do that! Would he?"

"Oh for goodness sake," she sighed, rolling her eyes in exasperation, "what's to stop the Caesar saying, for instance, that he'll only get rid of Caradoc and his tribe if we all double or even treble what we pay him now? That's the problem with paying people to fight your battles for you! If there is any danger of that happening, I say we ought to tell the Strangers to go back beyond the ninth wave and leave Caradoc to us. And another thing..." Prasutagus, sensing what was coming next, began to feel a little uneasy. "Caradoc might be an arrogant bighead, but it seems to me that he does have a point. Why should we let the Strangers just walk in here like they own the place? I mean," she blazed, "who do they think they are? We should say to them, thanks for the offer of help, but we really don't need you to see off the Catuvellauni for us. In fact we don't need your protection at all any more!"

Her husband put his head in his hands and groaned. Boudicca was quite right, of course: he could see that. But he knew that Antedios would never agree to such a reckless course of action and, to be quite honest, Prasutagus wasn't sure himself that he wanted to take on the whole of the Caesar's army.

"Gracious, Prasutagus," exclaimed Boudicca, "you're the most powerful warrior these lands have ever seen! What are you so worried about? Get out there, tell the Strangers to get lost and then teach Caradoc a lesson he won't forget. If you don't, I will!"

Prasutagus suddenly felt old and tired. "The endless wars between the people of these lands brought ruin and sorrow. I played my part in all of that, and so did your father. Between us we squandered wealth, youth and valour in the pursuit of what? Nothing but heads and vanity." He sat down on the edge of the bed and patted the space beside him.

"What are you saying?" she asked him.

Prasutagus took her hand in his and pressed it against his lips. "Have you ever heard the old proverb," he continued, "while we were out raiding our neighbours' cattle, a wolf crept into our enclosure to feast upon our lambs?"

Boudicca nodded. "Of course I have," she replied, "what's that got to do with anything?"

"Well, maybe it's time to just stay home and tend our flock." Looking into those amazing eyes, Prasutagus could tell that Boudicca was struggling to understand what he was trying to say. Well, he wasn't really sure either: all he knew for certain was that he didn't want to fight any more. Not Antedios, not Caradoc, not the Strangers.

***

Boudicca's slave Cara entered the chamber a little while before the first rays of day-light prised the cracks in the palisade. Smiling broadly, and dressed in her finest clothes ready for the feast, Cara roused Boudicca, helping her into her ceremonial dress; then she plaited the Queen's long, thick hair, while Boudicca nursed baby Briana.

"There is such a great gathering!" Cara was saying excitedly. "Oh, Lady, you should see how many people there are, and how happy they all are! I don't think I've ever seen anything like it! Why don't you bring the little princess outside to see the first flame? I'm sure everyone would love that!"

Boudicca was hardly listening to any of this, gently

stroking the top of Briana's head with her finger. "Cara," she said thoughtfully, "do you ever wish that you had the power to look into the future?"

"Oh lady," exclaimed Cara, who had been with Boudicca since they were both little girls and knew better than anyone the way her moods could change. "I think it's a curse to have the gift of foresight. It is so much better to live in expectation. Just think, you might discover that the sky is about to fall in, and then what would you do? You couldn't very well pretend to yourself that you didn't know, could you? You'd be too terrified to do anything except sit around and wait for it to happen!" Cara shuddered.

"Well, I wouldn't mind knowing. Then I could try and prevent it from happening," said Boudicca, firmly.

As Cara considered the wisdom of this reply, a great roar went up from the enclosure. The Druids had captured the first flame thrown down by the sun-god and ignited the Sacred Bonfires. Summer had returned to Icenia: it was officially the end of the darkness.

"But what if you couldn't prevent it from happening?" asked Cara, gently. "I mean, what if it was the will of the gods? What would you do then?"

Boudicca bit her lip and looked down into the dark eyes of her tiny daughter. "Oh, that's easy," she said. "You know the song of the Iceni warriors, don't you."

"But that's just a song, lady," Cara replied. "A song can't help you fight fate."

"It's not just a song; it's what I believe. And if you believe strongly enough, then nothing can ever hurt you." She rocked Briana in her arms and sang the song in a low voice, to a strong insistent rhythm:

I shall not be killed.
I shall not be hunted.
I shall not be captive;
I shall not be wounded.
Neither fire, nor sun, nor moon shall burn me.
Neither lake, nor river, nor sea shall drown me.

CHAPTER 2
Seed-fall
Samhain, 31st October, 43CE

" Now we must travel a little forward in time, through
the summer and then the autumn of that fateful year,
until we arrive at the eve of winter: the night upon
which we celebrate the Feast of Samhain and the start of the
New Year. Back in the old days, this was always an uncertain
time, but that particular Samhain the prospect seemed even
bleaker than usual. True, the Iceni stamped the soft earth
with their feet; scoured straight lines in the ground with
their hoes; gathered in their cattle, slaughtering those which
would not survive the winter, just as they had always done.
But as they did all of these familiar things, an unfamiliar
dread hung in the skies above them.

That day, as the people of Icenia prepared to salute the
sun-god who was leaving their skies to darkness once more,
the Strangers were right there among them. They were

hanging about the hill-fort in their shiny armour, drinking wine and playing at dice; chatting up the girls and giving out sweet figs dipped in honey to the children. Oh, they were being nice enough now, but nobody dared ask how long it was going to last.

The way I learned this part of the story, years afterwards from Finian the Bard, was that it was an exceptionally cold and damp Samhain: the mists rose thick and heavy from the marshes; nobody felt much like celebrating, choosing instead to stay in their huts with their beasts and children, huddled around their hearths.

The Strangers had arrived in four legions under a commander called Aulus Plautius, who was as unyielding and implacable as the metal on his chest. As battle raged on the borders of Icenia, Antedios and Prasutagus had stood side by side and announced to the entire tribe that nobody was to help the Catuvellauni in their desperate struggle against the Strangers.

Of course, they made sure that they had the full support of the Druids in this. Back then it was impossible to do anything without the Druids' say-so. There had been a ritual feast and the Salmon of Wisdom was eaten, a food which gave the Druids access to all the knowledge of our ancestors and power to divine the future. The Seer was able to tell the tribe that since their forefathers had made peace with the Caesar who had come a hundred years before, and since their forefathers had sworn to destroy the Catuvallauni, it

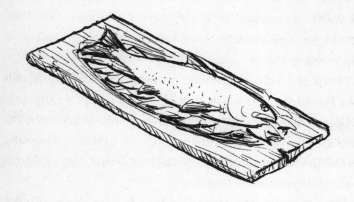

would be best to leave the Strangers to get on with the task of smashing Caradoc to pieces.

"The Strangers have come to claim the tribute stolen from them by that bloodthirsty pest Caradoc," announced Antedios. "This is no more than they are entitled to do, under the promise our forefathers made to render unto the Caesar what is his. This battle has nothing whatever to do with the Iceni: it is between the Strangers and the Catuvellauni; they must be permitted to fight it out between them."

Boudicca was standing there beside her father and her husband, but she wasn't prepared to make a secret of what she thought of her father's policy. When Antedios had said his bit, she stepped forward and raised her hands for hush.

"People of the Iceni," she declared in her loudest voice. "I'm afraid that the Strangers will use this as an excuse to demand more tributes from us!"

Prasutagus sighed. "Boudicca, please," he implored her, indicating the Druids who were standing beside him. "Let us do this in the way we agreed."

But a few of the more hot-headed young Iceni chieftains cheered her. "Queen Boudicca is right," said one of them, who went by the name of Aesunos.

"Aesunos! Aesunos!" the people shouted.

"Yes," said his friend Saenuvax, "we ought to go and smash up the Strangers while we've got the chance."

"Saenuvax, Saenuvax," yelled the crowd, along with "Boudicca! Boudicca!"

Antedios turned to the mob with a very stern expression. "You know," he announced, "anyone who wants to is free to leave Icenia any time, to go and help our enemy Caradoc – who has boasted so often about coming here in the dead of night and killing us all as we lie asleep in our beds," he said. "Go now: I won't stop you. Caradoc doesn't need your help, of course, but if you really want to put yourselves out, then I'm sure Aesunos and Saenuvax will see to it that your widows and orphans are well looked after."

The crowd who, a few moments before had been cheering the warriors, fell silent as they pondered the likelihood of this.

"You're all free," said the wily King, "to be traitors to your tribe at any time you wish. I'm quite content to let the gods judge you and your descendants!"

Antedios paused here for effect and looked around him at the assembled tribes-people; the cries of "Boudicca! Boudicca!" had begun to die down, and people were muttering quietly to one another. Seeing this, Antedios smirked.

"Or," he continued after a moment or two, "we can all sit here, have a feast and a drink or two, while the Strangers do all the work and see off Caradoc for us: after all, it's what we pay them to do. And once they've rid the land of that scourge," he continued, "I give you my word on oath that they will sail off beyond the ninth wave, and things will be just like they were before. Only better – because we won't have to worry about Caradoc any more."

There was a short silence while everyone thought about this, and then gradually the chanting began again, only this time the cries were for "Antedios! Antedios! Antedios!"

Boudicca glared disgustedly at the fickle tribes-people, but she knew when she was beaten. "I just hope I'm wrong and the Strangers are more stupid than they appear to be," she whispered to him as her father gave her a great big hug to prove to everyone that the whole royal family was of one accord.

***

46

Well, the battle between the Strangers and the Catuvellauni raged for two days, and not a single Iceni went to the assistance of either side. In fact, Queen Cartimandua of the Briganti tribe, who lived up in the Brown Lands, was the only one to help Caradoc, and everyone said that was only because she fancied him. In the end, the Strangers managed to drive Prince Caradoc into the Pale, the unknown lands that lie at the edge of the world, where the sun slips from the earth each night into the sea, and from where no man has ever returned alive.

When the news of Caradoc's defeat reached Icenia there was a huge sense of relief. But, as the weeks wore on the Strangers didn't seem to be in any hurry to leave. Far from it: in fact, once Aulus Plautius had seen off Caradoc and the Catuvellauni, the Caesar himself decided to pay a visit to these shores.

He arrived in the land of the Trinovanti with an even bigger army than the one Aulus Plautius had brought with him. Along with the kings of eleven other tribes, Antedios and Prasutagus were summoned to attend the Caesar and swear their loyalty to Rome. They met at a place down in the Red Lands where the earth rises up in great banks to protect the best pasture for miles around; a place the Catuvellauni and Trinovanti had long fought over because it afforded such good defence to the large settlement that lay beyond the dykes. It was called in those days the dunum, or fort, of Camulos, the war-god.

To welcome the Strangers the hearths of Camulodunum had been set with huge fires; spits laden with whole oxen and entire hogs; vast cauldrons of cawl; huge flagons of mead and sweet ale; piles of flat-cakes. But if the Kings ate at all it was with a bitter taste in their mouths.

Certainly, nobody who saw it would ever forget the awesome procession which attended the Caesar's arrival into Camulodunum. One who was there was Finian the Handsome. As one of King Prasutagus's Bards, and was there to make a good record of all the subsequent events.

In those days nothing was ever written down, instead the Bards made up long poems about everything that happened and committed them to their memory; then they would teach the poems to the Bards who came after them. It took twelve years to learn to sing over all the things that had ever happened, in the mean time even more events had taken place.

Finian's description of the visit of the Caesar exists only in my memory now, just as he taught it to me many years ago.

I can tell you a little of the poem, if you like:

Caesar came to Trinovantes.
With battle-rank and war-cry,
Power of horses, silver armour and shields,
Spearheads held high, they led the van:
Line upon line, beyond 6000 men.

Caesar came to Trinovantes,
With slaves from every corner of the earth.
Clay vessels filled with rose petals
To scatter on the road before him...

Now, like all the greatest Bards, Finian the Handsome was sometimes given to exaggeration, but even so I believed him when he told me that he had never seen anything like it in his whole life.

"What on earth are these creatures?" he asked, gesturing to one of the Strangers as a train of enormous beasts lumbered by.

"Elephantus," the fellow replied with a careless shrug.

Wow! thought Finian, these Strangers must be bold indeed, and their land full of many wonders if they can be so unimpressed in the presence of such an incredible animal!

Meanwhile, Prasutagus and the other Kings stood around the feasting chamber feeling quite overwhelmed by so many amazing sights. They had worn their most heavily patterned breeches and their most richly-woven cloaks; they had decorated their muscley bodies in the finest ceremonial way; and they had plaited their long hair, and streaked it with lime until it was rock hard. They all looked very splendid; yet, beside the Romans with their smart gold-edged tunics and their gleaming leather sandals and their clean-shaven chins, they somehow felt awkward and out of place.

All, that was, except for clever Antedios. He wasted no time in using his considerable cunning to ingratiate himself into the Caesar's confidence. As soon as the Caesar dismounted from his elephant, Antedios went straight up to him as if this was his hill-fort and not that belonging to the Trinovantean King. He clapped the Caesar on the back, before embracing him like a long-lost brother. Then, to the amazement of everyone, he addressed the great man in the Strangers' own tongue, knowing full well that none of the other Kings could understand a single word of what was being said.

Mind you, when the Caesar tried to speak a few words in our tongue it proved just as hard for everyone to understand. Apparently, Antedios later told Prasutagus, the Caesar had said that he had come in peace. He was also, it turned out, very keen to spend some time in Icenia itself, at Antedios's own hill-fort. A few days later he did so, staying for a full fortnight, and then another, and then still another, all the way through the Claim-time and the Arbitration-time: right up until the end of the Old Year.

"What are they saying?" Boudicca would demand to know, as night after night she watched her father and the Caesar deep in conversation.

"I wish I knew!" Prasutagus would sigh mournfully. "But they will insist on speaking in the Strangers' tongue, and even on the few occasions when the Caesar addresses me directly I have to rely on your father for a translation."

50

Boudicca knew her father very well. Although she loved him, she had no doubt that Antedios was plotting something, but as to what it was, she couldn't say for sure. One thing was clear, however: the Caesar believed that Antedios, was the true King of Icenia, and Prasutagus merely some sort of deputy.

Boudicca wasn't the only Icenian who mistrusted tricky Antedios in his dealings with the Caesar.

"They have come for our grain," the farmers muttered amongst themselves, as they poured the last of the harvest into the winter store pits. "It is well known they have a great need for grain, since they have vast armies in every corner of the earth, and there are not enough fields to feed them all."

"King Antedios is a fool for trusting the Strangers," the warrior chieftains, Aesunos and Saenuvax, grumbled to one another. "What we need is for Prasutagus to join with us so that we can send the Strangers packing. But he's afraid that if he does that, the Druids will make him suffer the four-fold death! What can we do? Our hands are tied!"

"The Strangers are politicians," observed the Druids shrewdly, shaking their wise heads in sorrow. "And truth does not abide with politics. The truthful man fights his own battles, but the politician thinks nothing of sending other men to fight on his behalf. Honour and strength are no match against clever plans and strategies. This being true, Antedios is perhaps the best man to deal with the Caesar: for he is the greatest politician these

51

lands have ever produced."

Prasutagus heard all this, and more, but ever mindful of his promise to Antedios and the Druids, he said nothing. Boudicca, however, watching with her steely eyes, had noticed how her husband swayed ever so slightly as he pulled away from greeting the Caesar. She noticed too how he had shrunk back from embracing the Caesar's champion, Aulus Plautius. And she noticed how Prasutagus did not let his eyes meet hers, brimming with questions, as he led the Caesar in a stately procession through the lines of chieftains into the banqueting hall each night.

***

"Perhaps the Strangers are the gods of the Otherworld, come to visit us for Samhain." Cara, Boudicca's maid, was pretty and kind, but sometimes, as today, Boudicca found her silly and annoying.

Cara had been a child when Iceni warriors had captured her during a raid on the Coritani tribe, who dwelt up in the Speckled Lands. She had been given to the young Boudicca as a gift by her father, who had grown concerned that she spent too much of her time fighting with the boys.

"Here's a pretty playmate for you," he'd announced to Boudicca, who put down her sword and shield for once and peered at the shy, dark-haired girl, not quite as tall as she was, who was crying bitterly for her mother.

"What's your name?" Boudicca had demanded, but the Coritani spoke a different tongue to the Iceni, and so the little girl had no idea what the tall, striking Princess was asking her, and had cried even more. But Boudicca had persisted. She pointed to herself and said her own name very loudly and distinctly. Then she pointed to the little girl and pronounced the word "cara", the old Icenian word for "friend". After a few minutes of this the little girl had stopped crying long enough to point back and say in a small voice "Boudicca", at which Boudicca had rewarded her with a big smile, clapping her hands delightedly.

"That's right!" she said encouragingly, "I'm Boudicca! Now – who – are – you –?" After a few moments' hesitation, the little girl pointed back at herself and said very quietly and uncertainly, "Cara", and from that moment onwards this was the only name she ever had.

The two women had grown up together, and they shared everything. Everyone should be blessed with such a loyal and loving friend as was Cara; and most of the time Boudicca appreciated her very much. But this morning, as Cara combed through Boudicca's thick hair with a silver comb, the girl's thinking aloud was making the fractious queen decidedly ill-tempered.

"Why does everyone talk about the Strangers in this fanciful way?" snapped Boudicca. "They're just men. Well, granted, they're hairier, and they don't bath as often as Icenian men do" – Cara couldn't help laughing at this – "but when it comes down to it, they're nothing special. I know that the gods have powers to shape-shift and play tricks on us, but I really don't believe that they would come to us in the guise of such hairy, smelly oafs!"

"Well, Majesty," said Cara, still laughing, "all I'm saying is that the veil between this and the Otherworld is very thin just now, and strange events do come to pass as the year changes."

"Oh Cara! You're talking rubbish as usual. I've spent hours with the Strangers every night, drinking the disgusting wine and horrible fish paste they brought with them, and I've yet to see anything remarkable about them at all. They're not as tall as our shortest turnspit! Trust me, these are no gods."

The two women had not noticed Prasutagus entering the chamber, and so Boudicca had no idea how long he had been standing behind her, before she caught a glimpse of him in her bronze mirror; but the moment she saw him she wished that she had held her tongue.

"I'm saddened to hear you speak this way about our guests," said Prasutagus in the quiet voice he used when he was most angry. "After all, it is the custom of our people to be hospitable to those we count as our friends." Boudicca turned to face him, her cheeks reddening with a surge of temper.

"I'll thank you not to remind me of my manners," she exclaimed indignantly. "I've sat there long into the night lis-

54

tening to the Strangers boasting about their conquests in battle, and I have smiled politely even though I didn't understand half of what they were saying. And yet I saw the Caesar yawn when our own champions did the same."

Prasutagus held up his hand, urging her to be quiet. "Caesar has brought us interesting gifts and wine and food from his great Empire."

"Pshaw!" spluttered Boudicca disdainfully, turning back to her mirror. She angrily gestured to Cara to finish dressing her hair, while Prasutagus stood silent in the chamber, stroking his long white moustaches.

"They have chased Caradoc far away from Icenia," he said at last. "And look how they've brought us together with our neighbours, the Trinovanti and the Atrebati, in friendship, ending the warring that has for so long been a curse upon our people."

Boudicca stared at him, open-mouthed. She had never heard Prasutagus talk like this before! Maybe Cara was right after all; maybe the Strangers were spirits from the Otherworld and they had enchanted the bravest warrior of the Iceni tribe!

"Have you completely lost your mind?" she exploded. "Can't you see what they're up to? They're just trying to trick you and father into thinking that they're your friends, plying you with their wine and flattery. Then, when you least expect it, they'll sneak back in here and steal everything we have. Only they won't have to sneak in, will they? No!

Because we've invited them in. Well, I say we ought to tell them to leave: right now!"

Prasutagus stood sadly in the entrance of the chamber. Cara didn't like the way he was looking at Boudicca.

"A queen should always be noble and proud," Prasutagus said with a sad sigh, "but it is never a good thing for anyone to be over-mighty." Then he turned and left without another word.

Cara knew her friend well enough to resist the urge to comfort her.

"I hate them," Boudicca said in a low voice. "I wish that they had never come here."

***

As it turned out, Boudicca did not have to wait long for the news she most wanted to hear. That very evening, at the special feast for Samhain, the Strangers announced that they intended to leave Icenia in a few days time, before the winds were too strong to carry them safely home. This was indeed great news, but it soon became clear that the Strangers were not prepared to leave everything in Icenia just as it had been before.

The first intimation that things were not to be as Antedios had promised came when, at the height of the celebrations, the Caesar's great champion, Aulus Plautius, rose up in front of everyone and announced that a legion would be sent into the Speckled lands and beyond; and that another would be sent through the lands of the defeated Catuvellauni all the way to the other great sea. Boudicca shot a glance at Prasutagus.

Caesar then turned to Antedios, smiling broadly, the way a wolf bares his teeth to a goose.

"Noble King Antedios," he declared, in his very bad Icenian, and in a tone which managed to make "noble" and "king" sound like insults. "This province," (which according to Finian the Bard was the very word he used) "this province has been neglected by us for too long. We wish to make amends: bring Britannia into the Empire and let all her people share in the great benefits which Rome has to bestow upon her loyal subjects."

Prasutagus was stroking his moustaches and looking hard at Antedios; but his co-ruler was beaming at the Caesar, as if only he mattered.

"Of course," the Caesar continued, "in order for Britannia to take its place in the Empire there will need to be some improvements."

Boudicca could no longer stop herself from crying out.

"Father," she cried, "what does this mean?"

Antedios winked and gestured at her to be quiet. Astonished, she looked across at Prasutagus. "What's wrong with you?" she hissed. "Icenia has two kings and it seems to me that neither of you is standing up for her."

"Let the Caesar finish what he has to say," said

Antedios, smiling all the while.

The Caesar had beckoned one of his retinue forward and the fellow was kneeling before him bearing a long scroll of cow hide, covered with strange markings. Antedios leant forward, pretending to make sense of the markings, but Boudicca could always tell when her dad was lying and showing off.

Watching him now, she felt her stomach do a flip.

"You will need roads, of course," said the Caesar, and Antedios nodded firmly in agreement. "And more and better forts."

"Naturally."

Prasutagus had started at the word "forts" and, seeing this, Boudicca sent a prayer to the goddess Andraste. At last, she thought, at last my husband is going to prove what a great warrior he is! She half-expected him to leap up and knock the Caesar's head off his shoulders there and then, but all Prasutagus did was clench his fists.

"The Imperial Legions will see to all of this," drawled the Caesar, "but of course it won't be cheap. Such benefits cost a great deal of money, as I'm sure you are aware, noble King."

"Oh, yes, yes, of course. Roads are very expensive things," said Antedios.

At this Prasutagus raised his head to speak. "So, this will mean more tributes for Rome, I suppose," he said. Prasutagus was using his quiet voice: the quiet of a snake about to swallow a mouse.

The Caesar stopped smiling. "Well, no, not exactly," he said, clearly irritated. "There are several very wealthy men in Rome who are prepared to pay the money so that Britannia can be transformed into a great province of the Empire."

"As a sort of gift, you mean, don't you, mighty Caesar?" said crafty Antedios.

"Well, no," replied Caesar flatly. "Not a gift: more of a loan."

Antedios frowned at this. Seeing his consternation, Aulus Plautius broke in quickly. "Oh, that's not something that need concern you, Noble King Antedios," he said, waving aside the murmurs of protest beginning to start up in the feasting chamber. "It's most unlikely that you will ever have to pay the money back – well at least not for years to come. Unless, that is, there is some unforeseen problem." Aulus Plautius took a few moments to look menacingly around the assembly. "And of course, the benefits that come with being a fully modernised province will more than realise the investment. I'll make quite sure of that."

"Not so fast," burst out Boudicca. She pointed rudely at Aulus Plautius, "what did he mean when he said: 'I'll make sure of that?' It sounded like some sort of a threat to me..."

The Caesar and his champion laughed at her outburst, but it was less easy to ignore Prasutagus.

"The Queen is right to ask that," he said in his quiet voice. "Ask them what they mean, Antedios: ask them how the Caesar's champion will 'make sure' of anything?"

The Caesar sighed in exasperation. "Well, you'll need someone to oversee the improvements, won't you?" he said as if he was addressing a very small and rather stupid child, "someone who understands how we do these things in the Empire. You know, you ought to be very pleased that a man of Aulus Plautius's considerable accomplishments has agreed to stay here and act in a supervisory capacity." At the mention of his name the champion bowed low to the Caesar.

"Please, Prasutagus," grimaced Antedios, "just leave this to me, will you? You don't even speak the language, do you?"

Prasutagus had to admit that he didn't – moreover, he had given his word never to challenge Antedios. Prasutagus sat back in his throne, silently stroking his moustaches; but he kept his eye on the Caesar's champion all the while.

For her part, Boudicca wasn't sure that she understood all of what was going on, but she could see that the Strangers had no intention of returning to Rome in a hurry, and that worried her. She watched with her heart in her mouth as the Caesar indicated the places on the scroll where he would like Antedios to make his mark. All the while Boudicca thought, "for the love of the goddess Andraste, father, please don't agree to anything stupid!" At last she could bear it no longer.

"Hold on a minute, father," she exclaimed. "You can't agree to anything on your own. Have you forgotten that

Prasutagus is as much King of Icenia as you are?"

Antedios looked up from the scroll. "Oh, my dear daughter," he smirked, "we might both be Kings of Icenia, but," and here a sly look came into his eyes, "I'm afraid that the Caesar has decided that I am to be the Client King for this province, and so he is prepared to deal with me only. It's out of my hands I'm afraid!" he said, shrugging in mock regret.

"Prasutagus! Don't stand for this," shrieked Boudicca at her husband. "Do something!"

Her husband looked hard at King Antedios, about to put his mark on the parchment scroll. Then he looked over at the Druids, who were shaking their heads and moaning in a corner. Then he looked at the other chieftains, who were all looking back at him, aghast: waiting for him to give his command to kill the Caesar, all his retinue, and the treacherous Antedios.

"Oh dear," thought Prasutagus. "It seems like whatever I do, I'm done for."

And that was when he looked at Boudicca. She was glaring at him in that way she did when he had tried her patience too much.

"I can't, Boudicca," he shrugged. "I can't take on your father. I gave my word."

Antedios, meanwhile, had heard everything, and was sitting there chuckling triumphantly, with the Caesar on one side and Aulus Plautius on the other. "Never mind,

Boudicca," he said, waving dismissively at Prasutagus. "Waste not your regret for him. This agreement I've just made, means that you and I can rule all of Icenia between us, and if anyone doesn't like it," he continued turning to look at the Druids and the chieftains, "well, they can take it up with my friend the champion Aulus Plautius here, and the men of the IInd and IXth Legions!"

Boudicca roared at him.

"What?" spluttered Antedios, surprised by the fury in her eyes; the anger in her voice. "What is it, darling? Don't you want to be Queen any more?"

"Father," bawled Boudicca, "you've done some pretty low things in your time, but this has got to be the worst of all. How could you betray Prasutagus in this way? How could you betray the Iceni? How could you betray me?"

Then she flung herself down on the ground and wept as though her heart would break.

Prasutagus came and knelt beside her. He stroked her hair and whispered that really things were not as bad as all that.

"We still have each other, my love," he said. Boudicca turned her head sharply to look at him.

"And as for you," she gasped. "I thought you were a hero! I thought you were the bravest warrior in all Icenia."

With that, Boudicca rose abruptly and ran from the banqueting hall.

***

It was cold in the enclosure. Boudicca wrapped her cloak around her and took a few deep breaths. The air was bitter with the scent of decay.

She had not been aware of the Augury standing in the darkness in front of her, and she jumped, startled, when the crone's hand gripped her arm.

"What is it? What do you see?" Boudicca could tell at once that the woman had the sight of something in her soot-black eyes. The Augury looked straight through the Queen as if she wasn't there, and then she started to laugh like a jay bird. She gripped Boudicca's arm so tightly that the blood stopped flowing through it.

"I see," said the Augury, "summer without flowers. Cattle without milk. I see... warriors without courage. I see... people without a king, sea without fish, woods without trees. I see. I see..." Then she let out a terrible wail. Boudicca's heart pounded as panic gripped her. "Oh! Mighty Andraste, I pray, I beg you," screamed the Augury, "make me blind that I may see no more."

Using all her strength, Boudicca prised the woman's fingers from her arm, and then she turned and ran, not stopping until she reached the safety of her bed chamber. Snatching Briana from the crib, she clasped the child tightly to her.

"Lady," cried Cara, her soft dark eyes wide in alarm,

"whatever is wrong – have you seen a spirit?" Boudicca grabbed Cara's hand, and together the two women sat on the edge of the bed.

"Oh, Cara!" cried Boudicca, "I am afraid that Briana will never be Queen. I am afraid that Caesar intends to take Icenia for himself."

"Oh hush, lady. How could that be?"

"I am afraid that we will all be taken as slaves…"

Cara smiled sweetly. "Remember, lady, that I'm a slave. Do you remember how when I first came to you I was so afraid? How I used to cry for my mother every night? But you were kind to me. You told me how much you missed your mother too – do you remember that? And you said that as long as we were together we would always look after one another, and we wouldn't need our mothers any more." Cara kissed Boudicca on the top of her head and smoothed her hair. "Well, I've never completely forgotten my home, nor my real family, but I've grown to love you, and being part of your family."

"No!" gasped Boudicca, drawing Briana closer to her. "Why, I would rather kill my child, my beloved Briana, with my own hands than see her taken into captivity!"

CHAPTER 3
Claim-time
Lughnasadh, 31st July, 47CE

❝ Well, like the Caesar, the year came and went; then another and another, and before long it was summertime once again and the Strangers had been in our midst for four years. The Iceni hardly thought about them at all any more. I suppose it is just as sensible Cara said: you really can get used to anything, given enough time.

For one thing, the Strangers were too busy fighting Prince Caradoc and what remained of the Catuvellauni far off in the Pale Lands to bother much with what the Iceni were getting up to. And even when they were not doing that, the closest Aulus Plautius and his legions ever came to Icenia was to spend time in their enormous fort at Camulodunum, down in the Red Lands. Unless you had to go there for some reason, it was perfectly possible to live in Icenia and never see a Stranger from one end of the year to the next.

As the years went by people began to wonder what all the fuss had been about. The Strangers built these lovely, straight roads all over the place; roads which hardly ever got so muddy that your cartwheels got stuck in them. And what's more, these roads hadn't cost Icenia a penny. They were paid for out of the "loans", just as the Caesar had promised. Although at the time Antedios had been widely criticised for signing the agreement with the Caesar without consulting Boudicca and Prasutagus, a good many Icenians now thought that he had done the right thing.

With Caradoc out of the way it was possible to travel well beyond the Yellow Lands without fear of being killed; people began to think nothing of going to Camulodunum or Verulamium, and even Londinium, and they went not in order to kill their neighbours and steal their stuff, as they used to do, but to trade with them. In fact, thanks to the roads, trading became the new thing, and as a result the tribes-people began to grow wealthier, which made them happier and easier to rule over.

King Antedios was very pleased indeed with himself. He liked it when everyone said he was the greatest King who ever lived. Of course, he had to satisfy Aulus Plautius (who was now officially Governor of Britannia) that the Iceni were loyal to Rome, but all he had to do in that regard was to use some of the tribes' increasing wealth to pay the tribute. It was all so easy! Perhaps, you might think, too easy.

And that was what Boudicca was worried about. She had never forgiven her father for tricking Prasutagus and doing a sneaky deal with the Strangers. And she still didn't trust the Strangers. Things might be very nice in Icenia, but it was well-known that if you were to travel a short distance beyond the Yellow Lands, the Strangers were a much more prominent and far less benign presence. Every so often someone would return from trading with news of a battle at which the Strangers had brutally put down a local chieftain and his warriors.

The fort at Camulodunum, for example (where Aulus Plautius had his headquarters), had been built by enslaved Trinovanteans, and the local people had to do whatever the Strangers told them or they were beaten up. The legionaries swaggered about the town doing whatever they liked.

"And what's the real idea behind all these roads and forts they're building everywhere?" Boudicca wondered. "Mighty Andraste! I wish I knew. The Strangers are so clever, there just has to be something in it for them."

When her father heard her talk like this, he would try and explain to her about the agreement he had struck with the Caesar, and how if she would only see sense and ditch Prasutagus they could both reap the benefit.

"You're a fool," she would tell her father, "and the Caesar's a fat bully. He's used to getting his own way, and he doesn't do anything unless it's of some benefit to him."

Antedios patted her on the head, which always made her

furious. "Don't you worry, my dear. As long as we behave ourselves and keep the Caesar sweet, he won't bother us. He's given us the roads so we can get on with making ourselves as wealthy as possible, and keep on paying him the tribute. Trust me: I understand how the mind of a great King works better than any one in these lands. That's why the Caesar took to me straight away."

Her father's boasting made Boudicca feel sick. And it worried her that everyone else, including Prasutagus, was prepared to go along with him. Often she would find herself thinking about the scroll Antedios had put his mark to, and how long it would be before the Strangers came calling, asking for the agreement to be honoured.

"I wonder what he promised them?" she would ponder. "I wonder what we have that the Caesar would want more than anything else?"

Gold? Grain? Slaves? Cattle? Icenia had so many treasures. Whenever she asked Antedios, he would simply wink at her and murmur something about how she had nothing to worry about and he had seen to it that her interests were taken care of. It wasn't long before Boudicca came to the troubling conclusion that her father probably had no idea himself what he had agreed to. It was perfectly possible for the Caesar to have flattered him into agreeing to just about anything.

Another thing worried her. Now that they didn't have to fight any more the Iceni champions, once so tough and scary, had begun to grow fat and lazy. Prasutagus was always exercising, and very careful about how much he ate, so he appreciated at once what Boudicca was saying when she pointed it out to him. He imposed fines on a few of the champions, placed them on short rations, and ordered them to engage in mock-contests with one another, but it would take a bit more than that to make them fighting fit, if the Strangers decided to attack. The warriors moaned about the new regime; they blamed Queen Boudicca, and soon her popularity amongst the tribe was at an all-time low.

In spite of this, however, Boudicca and Prasutagus had, along with the rest of the tribe, a good and comfortable life. And ever since that terrible night when Antedios had tricked them, they had, if anything, come to love and appreciate each other even more. Within two years of the Caesar returning to Rome, they were blessed with another daughter, Ardra, the noble. Meanwhile, their first, Briana, was growing into a strong, beautiful and very wilful child, all of which pleased her mother and father very much.

And so summer came around again, the Feast of Lughnasadh, when the harvest is gathered and everyone enjoys the long days of warmth and sunshine.

Queen Boudicca always loved the summer months. She loved feeling the warmth of the sun-god's flames on her face and arms, and she loved breathing the air sweetened with ripening fruit. Most of all she loved to stand outside the fort, and look down from the hill-top on to the seemingly endless spread of golden wheat below.

The Feast of Lughnasadh, in keeping with the languor of the season, was not at all frantic, like the other feasts of those days. It was a lovely, gentle, sleepy feast, and that afternoon the warmth and stillness of the air settled like a silky web over everything. Boudicca had gone to meet the little princesses, who had been with Cara to watch the harvest being gathered, and she was looking forward to spending the rest of the day relaxing with Prasutagus and her daughters as the sun shone late into the evening.

This was only Briana's fourth summer and yet everyone was already saying she had the true bearing of a queen. Nobody would ever say the same of little Ardra, but she was a good and sweet-natured child. Cara had plaited flowers in their long coppery hair and Boudicca must have smiled when she saw them dancing happily as they returned to the fort.

As the girls reached their mother, she scooped them up and covered them with her thick red hair. The princesses were excited about the coming feast and looking forward to making little figures of the corn-god out of plaited stalks. Boudicca and Cara were promising to help them when the low, mournful caw of the guard's horn burst forth from the watchtower behind.

"What's happened, lady?" asked Cara, startled. But Boudicca knew no more than she did. The four of them hurried back into the protection of the fort. It was there they learned that a small group of Strangers was approaching the bottom of the hill.

The enclosure was full of people preparing for the Feast. Women and children were making loaves and corn-god figures, every surface spread with oatcakes and eggs and flowers. Everyone was busy, but in spite of the news the mood was calm. Nobody showed the slightest bit of alarm when Boudicca ran through yelling at them to take arms and run to the great chamber because the Strangers were coming. Most people looked at her as if she was mad; they shrugged to one another and carried on with whatever it was they were doing.

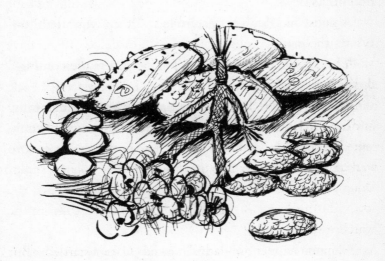

Boudicca told Cara to take the frightened Princesses into the relative safety of the bedchamber and then raced towards the great hall shouting for Prasutagus. At the entrance she almost tripped over a warrior who was taking a sly nap in the shade. The furious Queen gave him a thump across the top of his head.

"Hey you!" she roared at him. "What's the matter with you? You great lazy idiot. Get up! The Strangers are coming! What's the matter with everyone! Am I the only one who isn't in some sort of a daze?" The warrior hauled himself on to his feet, but he was much more annoyed at having had his snooze so rudely interrupted, than alarmed by Boudicca's news.

"Alright, alright," he grumbled. "Keep your hair on. What's the panic?"

"The Strangers are coming! The Strangers are coming!" shrieked Boudicca, pounding her fists on the warrior's back and shoulders. She looked him up and down disdainfully. "By the Mighty Andraste, you ought to be ashamed of yourself," she snarled. But like everyone else in the enclosure, the warrior didn't seem to care one bit what she thought.

***

As it happens it was only a small group of legionaries, seven ordinary men and a Praefectus, who marched smartly into the great chamber, but they brought massive news.

"Let it be known," bawled the Praefectus, "that in recognition of his great distinction in the art of war, the first Consular Governor of the Province of Britannia, Aulus Plautius, has been summoned back to Rome to receive an ovation at the Forum in accordance with the great honour he has earned in the service of the Empire, and that henceforth Publius Ostorius Scapula will serve as Consular Governor of the Province of Britannia!"

"What's he shouting about?" Boudicca asked her father, who was looking rather concerned. As Antedios relayed the news to the gathering of Iceni, the Praefectus unfurled a large scroll of parchment, and the seven men who had escorted him jogged together, forming a protective circle around him. They faced outwards, their hands resting menacingly upon the hilts of their daggers.

"Oh dear," muttered Antedios anxiously. "I don't like the look of this."

Prasutagus leant forward in his throne, watching intently as the Praefectus read from the scroll in his own tongue, smoothing his long white moustaches between his thumb and forefinger in slow deliberate strokes. Boudicca, kneeling at his feet, watched him closely, but the old warrior's eyes gave nothing away.

The proclamation made, the Praefectus rolled up the parchment and spoke some more words to Antedios. Boudicca noted with concern how her father had turned quite pale. Then, as swiftly as they had arrived, the Strangers turned around and marched off back to their fort at Camulodunum.

"That was bad news, wasn't it?" said Prasutagus to his old enemy, as soon as the legionaries had gone.

Antedios put his head in his hands and sat groaning. "What is it?" Boudicca cried. "What do they want from us? Father, tell us what's wrong!"

Eventually Antedios spoke. "The new governor," he said in a halting voice, "the new governor... Oh by the great sun-god, I don't know how to say this..." Antedios sighed heavily. "The new governor has made a law forbidding the native warriors of these islands to carry weapons."

Everyone gasped, and then they all began shouting at once.

"They've done what?" burst out Boudicca, "I knew it. I knew they were up to something. Those sneaky wolves. Father, how could you have been so stupid as to trust them?"

The chieftains were going wild: Aesunos and Saenuvax were jumping up and down and shaking their fists at Antedios. Outside in the enclosure, the Druids were running around the great bubbling cauldron prepared for the Feast; their hands raised to the skies, they called upon the gods to avenge the people.

A savage cry went up: "Kill the Strangers! Kill the Strangers! Kill the Strangers!"

"The warriors of the Iceni will never give up our

weapons!" yelled Aesunos.

"We will die before we disarm!" yelled Saenuvax.

Boudicca was thrilled to see the Iceni warriors hopping mad for once, instead of lazing about in the sunshine. It was just like the old times. She looked across at Prasutagus, but her husband didn't look at all happy.

Moreover, things were not looking too good for Antedios. The furious chieftains had surrounded the terrified King.

"This is all your fault, Antedios," Aesunos was shouting.

"He deserves to die like the treacherous dog he is," shouted Saenuvax.

"Yes! Kill Antedios!" howled Aesunos.

"Kill Antedios! Kill Antedios!" chanted the tribes people.

Boudicca felt a pang of pity as she caught a glimpse of her dad's terrified face.

Then Prasutagus held up his hand and everyone fell silent.

"Leave him alone," commanded the mighty warrior King, and Aesunos, who had seized the whimpering Antedios by the scruff of his neck, dropped him to the floor like a sack of flour.

"Antedios is still King of Icenia," said Prasutagus in his quiet voice, "and if any of you want to challenge that, you will have to get past me first."

Aesunos stepped forward. "He's betrayed us," he shouted, "he's let the Strangers walk in here and take our weapons. I say we kill the dog."

"Yes," said Saenuvax against the roars of the other chieftains, "we will never surrender to the Strangers. If Antedios loves them so much, let's stick him in a coracle and send him beyond the ninth wave so that he can live with them in their own lands for ever more."

"Oh, but surely there's no need for that. Is there?" said a quivering Antedios. He had picked himself up from the ground and was dusting himself off, trying to gather his wits and his dignity. He smiled imploringly at Prasutagus. "It's some misunderstanding, that's all. When my friend the Caesar hears about it, he'll sort it out. You'll see."

"No, Antedios!" said Prasutagus firmly, and Boudicca felt a thrill run down her spine to see her beloved husband take control of the situation. "There's to be no more depending upon the Caesar. We must fight our own battles from now on; something we should have done a long time ago."

"I say, we ask the Druids to determine the fate of Antedios," Aesunos suddenly roared, to a great cheer of approval. This was not good: back in those days when things were going badly for a tribe it was the custom to blame the King, and blaming the King usually meant sacrificing him to one or other of the gods in order that the spell of bad luck might be broken. Antedios fell on his knees and begged the warriors for mercy.

"No! No! Not the Druids!" he pleaded. "Anything but that!"

It all happened so quickly. Before anyone had a chance to

76

stop it the terrified king had been bundled up and carried out into the enclosure.

"Help!" cried Antedios. "Prasutagus! Boudicca! Help me!"

"Leave him alone," commanded Prasutagus. "Put him down! He's still your King!"

"Let him go!" shrieked Boudicca, running after them. "Let him go!"

But it was too late. By the time Boudicca and Prasutagus had managed to fight their way through the baying crowd, the Druids had already started their awful ritual. Boudicca reached the front of the mob just in time to see her father tipped into the giant cauldron. All she could do was watch helplessly, while poor, foolish Antedios was boiled, his agonised screams drowned by the cheers and shouts of the warriors.

***

"To begin with," King Prasutagus told the gathering of the tribe later that evening, "we'll build a secret fort out in the salt-marshes, hidden by the mists and the reed-beds. We'll take as much of our treasure as we can carry and hide it there."

"Hide our treasure?" the tribes-people complained. "Why should we hide our treasure?"

"Well, if you'd rather, you could just give it all to the

Strangers," said Prasutagus in his quiet voice. He waited for the murmurs of disagreement to die down before continuing with the outline of his plan. "Then," he said, "we'll hide a store of weapons there, too."

"Hold on a minute!" shouted Aesunos. "I'm not going to hide my weapons!"

"No, nor me," yelled Saenuvax.

Prasutagus fixed them both with his cold, hard stare. He was in no mood to take any more nonsense from anyone. "Listen to me, you young hot-heads," he said coolly. "I'm in charge now, and I say we're not ready to fight a battle with the Strangers. Not yet." He waited for the resulting clamour to die down. "Look at you, Aesunos," he said mockingly. "Why, your stomach is fatter than a pig's. And, as for you Saenuvax, you've been drinking far too much honey wine this summer. Little Princess Briana has better muscles and a sharper mind than either of you." Everyone laughed at this, which soon shut the two bothersome chieftains up.

Prasutagus sat back in his throne and watched them all keenly. "What a bunch," he thought to himself. "Maybe it would be best if I just left them for the Strangers to control after all." Unfortunately, that wasn't a serious option. Prasutagus was the sole King of the Iceni now and it was his job to ensure the tribe's survival. "First off, we need to get fit," he continued. "And that means all of us. Every man, woman and child will be on short rations and there will be exercises every morning in the enclosure here, and swimming every afternoon. And while we're getting fit, we'll make it look as though we're going along with the Strangers' demands so they don't suspect anything and force us into a battle before we're ready. We'll give in a few of our weapons, just as they've asked us to do – only enough to satisfy them that we're being obedient – the rest we'll hide away in the secret fort until we're ready to use them."

The Iceni warriors discussed the merits of this plan amongst themselves: loudly, naturally. In those days everything had to be argued about; usually fought about too.

"I don't know," said Aesunos. "It looks like we're giving in, and the Iceni never give in."

"Yes, I know that," groaned Prasutagus, "but we want the Strangers to think that we're obedient again."

"By the great sun-god," he thought, "why are they all so stupid?"

"Look, I might not be as clever and tricky as poor old Antedios was, but I have learned a few things by watching him over the past few years. Going off haring about the place killing everyone – trust me, that approach just won't work with the Strangers."

His words were wasted on the stubborn tribesmen: a terrible din was got up as they began running about the place all shouting.

"We're not afraid of the Strangers!" shrieked Saenuvax.

"We're fearless!" shouted everyone else. "We're brave Iceni warriors! We're the greatest!"

"Shut up you lunatics!" Prasutagus thundered. "Listen for a moment will you? The Strangers are nowhere near as brave and fearless as we are, but they have a lot of other things going for them. To begin with they're really sly and cunning; then there are loads of them – for every one that's here there are twenty more waiting over the ninth wave; they have good weapons too; and, they are well-organised." He scanned the rowdy mob standing in front of him: their half-naked bodies daubed in blue paint; their lime-streaked hair sticking up all over the place; the clashing patterns of their breeches and tartan cloaks.

Prasutagus sighed. "The Strangers love everything to be tidy and in its place," he said, shaking his head ruefully, "and we – well, we don't. Look at the way they all wear exactly the same outfits, and all have the same haircuts; look at how they all march together in step."

"Yeah! Like little kids at a Beltane dance!" sneered Aesunos.

"Except that they're armed to the teeth and are always thinking two or three steps ahead. No little kid dances like that. And if we want to beat them we're going to have to spend a bit of time getting not only stronger, but sneakier too: we're going to have to learn how to plan ahead, just like they do. If we rush in and fight them now, they'll just crush us like worms under their – what do they call them? – their sandals."

Prasutagus had the attention of the people now.

"Now," said the mighty warrior King, turning to Finian the Bard. "I have a job for you, lad."

Finian bowed deeply. "I will compose a great poem, mighty lord, so that our descendants will all know how great you are."

"Yes, yes," said Prasutagus, "of course you must do that; but there's something else I want you to do. I want you to go back to Trinovantes, and tell the King to meet with me."

"Great!" said Aesunos. "Are we going to kill the Trinovanti as well!"

Prasutagus sighed deeply. "No, Aesunos, we're not going to kill the Trinovanti. As a matter of fact we're going to join forces with them."

"What?" spluttered Saenuvax, almost choking on his horn flask of mead.

"My grand-dad's head," said Aesunos in deadly earnest, "is still decorating the walls of the Trinovanti feasting chamber. He'll come and haunt me at Samhain if he knows I let the Iceni join forces with our mortal enemies!"

Prasutagus groaned. Being King was really difficult sometimes... "Look, the Strangers are our mortal enemy now, not the Trinovanti," he said in his quiet voice. "As a matter of fact the Trinovanti are pretty fed-up that they never got given back all the land that Caradoc stole from them. Instead, the Strangers kept it for themselves and now it's impossible to fart in the Red Lands without asking for their permission." Everyone laughed, including Aesunos and Saenuvax. "The Trinovanti are treated like slaves in their own lands," said Prasutagus unsmiling. "They are forced to work in the fort at Camulodunum, and they don't like it, but we could use them to help us to get in there so we can steal more of those fantastic weapons that the Strangers have. And after a while we can start to make real nuisances of ourselves as far as the Strangers are concerned."

There was more fervent discussion amongst the warriors on this point, but Prasutagus could see that he had won the argument.

A strong king, he knew, should never need to force his tribe to do anything. He had to manage things so that the people decided to go along with him, as though of their own free will. That was the best way for a king to govern, and right now Prasutagus appeared to have all the makings of a great king.

Soon the chamber was ringing with cheers of "Prasutagus! Prasutagus!", but for once he wasn't all that thrilled to hear it. Prasutagus, you see, knew that he still had a long struggle ahead of him.

Queen Boudicca knew it too. She had been sitting quietly on her throne beside him all this while, with Briana and Ardra curled up asleep on her lap. They were too little to understand what had happened to their grandfather; all they knew was that they would never see him again. This news had upset them, but much, much worse had been the piteous howling of their mother, who, soon after Antedios's killing, had become so distraught that even Prasutagus could not comfort her. For hours Boudicca had done nothing except cling to the little Princesses and sob.

Even so, although completely exhausted and full of dread and foreboding, Boudicca insisted on taking her place beside Prasutagus as he addressed the tribe.

As she sat there listening to him outline his plan, Boudicca felt proud of her husband, but at the same time she was feeling completely disgusted with the fickle tribespeople.

"Look at them," she whispered to Cara, who was sitting at her feet. "One minute they're all over you and the next minute they hate you." She felt her eyes burn with sorrow.

CHAPTER 4
Song-time
Autumn Equinox, 21st September, 47CE

"Even though he was in his palace in Rome, far away beyond the ninth wave, the Caesar always paid particular attention to news from the Province of Britannia. That miserable little clump of gloomy islands was proving much more difficult and expensive to control than he would ever have imagined. That maniac Prince Caradoc was still giving the men of the IXth and XXth Legions a bashing in the remote Pale Lands, and now he had help from two of the most savage tribes of the region: the small, dark and fearless Ordovici and Siluri. All of this was bad enough. Far more troubling, however, as far as the Caesar was concerned, was the news that ever since Aulus Plautius had left, those previously well-behaved little dolts, the Iceni, had started to make a real nuisance of themselves, in all sorts of irritating and time-consuming ways.

The Caesar had always been of the opinion that it was a good idea to make an ally of at least one powerful person whenever you marched into a place and took it over. The Empire, you see, was enormous and he couldn't be everywhere at once. He could put governors in charge, but it was very useful to have someone local on hand to help: someone who could exercise a bit of control over the natives; someone dependable and easy to manipulate.

This plan had worked really well over half the world, by now, and it had seemed to be working a treat in Britannia, too. That idiot King Antedios could always be relied upon to do whatever he was told, and to keep his vast tribe of barbarians safely out of the way while the Caesar's great army gradually took the place over. Britannia was a real challenge, with its terrible food and weather, thick forests, misty plains, and its population of lunatics who didn't seem to care too much if they lived or died. Without dupes like Antedios, the tough job facing the Caesar would have been a million times harder.

"But I don't get it," said the genuinely perplexed Caesar when he received the latest news from Britannia. "When Aulus Plautius left Britannia, the Iceni were on our side. What's gone wrong? Why are they causing all this trouble? And why are the Trinovanti helping them? I thought these barbarian tribes all hated each other. Divide and rule! That's the way! We can't have them ganging up with each other against us: that will never do." The Caesar was growing more and more agitated; he thumped his fist down on the arm of his chair. "By the mighty Jove!" he thundered. "What's happening over there? What does that old fool King Antedios think he's playing at?"

"I'm afraid, mighty Caesar," explained one of his advisors, nervously looking up from another bit of news just in from the province, "that is to say: it appears that King Antedios was boiled alive by his tribes-people."

At first the Caesar was appalled: "These barbarians are worse than wild beasts!" Then he remembered something, and a sly look came over his features. "Dead eh?" he mused. "Well, now, that is most interesting. Now, look here, we have a lot of money tied up in the place, and I'm not prepared to risk a penny of it. Tell Ostorius Scapula that he had better sort the situation out, quick. I want the Iceni back on our side as soon as possible."

And so it was that at the end of the Arbitration Time, the governor Ostorius Scapula arrived at the Iceni fort with a centuria of eighty armed legionaries.

"You know we really ought to be friends," Ostorius Scapula said to Prasutagus as they greeted each other, "it's pointless us fighting when, if we got together again, we could easily conquer those idiots the Catuvellauni, not to say the Trinovanti and all the rest of them. Why, the Iceni are a great and noble people, just like us! You're the best tribe in the whole province. We could easily run this place between us and we'd all be a lot better off!"

Prasutagus stroked his moustaches thoughtfully while the governor spoke. The offer of reconciliation had caught him by surprise and he wasn't sure what to make of it. Boudicca, sitting on her throne next to him, was adamant that the Strangers could never be trusted and that this was most likely some sort of a trick.

The rest of the tribe, however, was only too willing to fall for all the flattering things that the governor was saying about the Iceni being the greatest. Aesunos and Saenuvax led the cheers when Ostorius Scapula said his bit about how they ought to be in charge of all the other tribes.

Even the Druids seemed to think that the governor's words spelt victory for Icenia. They had been staring at the sky and throwing the knuckle bones of a pig on to the ground all morning: the augurs were all absolutely positive.

Prasutagus, however, was far from sure about any of this. Mmmm, he thought. In order to get the better of the Strangers I need to try and think more like they do: now, if I was the governor what would I say to this offer of reconciliation?

"Remember," hissed Boudicca, "the Strangers never do anything without expecting even more back in return."

"Clever Boudicca!" thought Prasutagus. "OK," he said at last, "suppose the Iceni promise to go back to being loyal to the Caesar, what do we get in return?" he coolly asked the governor.

Ostorius Scapula's friendly smile vanished quicker than

the sun on a cloudy day. "How about," he said coldly, "we promise not to come back and kill you all."

But Prasutagus was not easily intimidated: like all great warriors he understood the importance of making threats as well as any Stranger. "Fine," he said in his quiet voice. "If that's the way you want it: the deal's off. Now, where do you want to fight?"

Ostorius Scapula knew when he was beaten. He didn't want to have to fight another protracted battle with another bunch of crazies, so he decided it was time to try another way. The Caesar had told him just what to do.

On his signal, a servant came forth bearing a great chest, from the depths of which the governor pulled out a long scroll, the very same which Antedios had put his mark on several years before.

"It says here," explained the governor, indicating some part of the document, "that on the death of King Antedios half of his kingdom would be rendered unto the mighty Caesar, hailed Imperator in the field, Father of his country, in recognition of his great achievement in bringing the barbarian tribes across the Ocean to the rule of the Roman people."

Boudicca gasped. Prasutagus was also very shocked to hear this, but he made a better job of covering up his feelings.

The two of them had often wondered what it was exactly that Antedios had agreed to, but neither of them had ever guessed that he would have done anything this enormous.

The great warrior King thought as quickly as he could.

"He's making it up," hissed Boudicca. "Father would never have agreed to that!"

But Prasutagus wasn't so sure.

"Antedios might have been tricked by the Caesar," he whispered. But it didn't matter much now in any case: not one person in the whole tribe could decipher the Strangers' marks, so how could he possibly challenge what the governor claimed was on the scroll?

"I think," he whispered to the Queen, "that we're going to have to take him at his word. If your father really did make this agreement, we'll have to honour it." Prasutagus looked very hard at the governor, trying to read the truth in his features, but it was difficult. The governor met his most powerful glare unflinchingly.

"Come along!" the governor said impatiently. "We don't have all day you know."

"What about the other half?" Queen Boudicca burst out. She pointed disdainfully at the scroll. "What does it say there about the rest of Icenia?"

The governor looked surprised at first, but then he threw back his head and roared with laughter. "Well, I don't think I need waste my time trying to broker deals with a man who can't even control his own wife," he sneered, before giving the order to have the scroll and the chest taken away.

Boudicca's face burned with rage. "I am my father's sole heir," she said quietly and with great dignity, "and I am Queen of Icenia. Surely, even under the customs of your own land, I have a right to know what is to be the fate of my rightful inheritance."

"Queen Boudicca is right," declared Prasutagus. "We render unto the Caesar only what is his. Antedios is dead and of course we must honour the pledge he made in respect of the portion of Icenia that belonged to him. But as to the rest of these lands, they belong to me and to Queen Boudicca, and when we die they will belong to our daughters. If the Caesar wishes the people of the Iceni to be loyal to him, then he will take what is his and no more. In return we give our word to stop the rebellion. That is to be the agreement. There's nothing more to discuss."

The governor slammed shut the lid of the chest, making a great show of anger, but only Queen Boudicca saw a sly smile creep across his face.

"We'll be back in the morning to take what is ours," he declared. "Half of this land belongs to us now, and as for the other half: well, if you want to keep a hold of that then you lot had better behave yourselves." And with that he turned and led his guard out of the fort and back to Camulodunum.

CHAPTER 5
Stay-at-home-time
Oimelc, 31st January, 60CE

❝Well, the years went by: twelve of them, all running the one into the other. A great deal happened during that time: to begin with, the princesses Briana and Ardra grew from little girls into young women, both tall like their mother, with the same noble bearing, long, thick red hair and flashing grey eyes. In every other respect, however, they were as different from one another as it is possible for two sisters to be. Briana was bright, and never happier than when she was riding hard across the misty plains with a spear in her hand; whereas Ardra preferred to sit quietly, playing her harp and singing. In spite of their differences the two sisters loved one another dearly; and they both loved their father and mother, too.

Prasutagus and Boudicca ruled wisely over Icenia in all those years, and did all they could to ensure that their beloved daughters would one day be great Queens in their own right. Of course, they never stopped worrying about what the future would bring, but they tried to be thankful for what they had, and most days life was as good as it had ever been.

Around them, however, things were changing. To begin with, after eight years of fighting, Prince Caradoc had finally been defeated. The bloodthirsty pest, and his family and followers were all put in chains, and sent over the ninth wave to face the Caesar. They expected to die an awful death, but as it turned out, the Caesar was very impressed with Caradoc's courage and he decided not to kill him after all. Instead he gave Caradoc a nice villa to live in, on condition, of course, that the Prince stayed far away from Britannia forever.

When Prasutagus heard this he said that it was foolish of the Caesar to reward Caradoc in this way; that it would only encourage loads of other young hotheads, like Aesunos and Saenuvax for example, to stir up trouble. But Boudicca thought it was very clever of the Caesar to deal with Caradoc like that: turning a feared warrior into a pet was the worst punishment ever.

Praustagus sighed and shook his head when she told him how she would rather die than surrender to the Caesar as Caradoc had done. "Perhaps," he said, "Caradoc was tired of fighting all the time. Maybe, he'd just had enough."

Boudicca hated it when Prasutagus spoke like this, which

he was doing more and more as he grew older.

Not long after the capture of Caradoc, the news reached Icenia that the Caesar had died and another Caesar had now taken his place as the most powerful ruler in the whole world. When he learned this Praustagus had sat up deep into the night stroking his moustaches and staring into the fire. In the morning he ordered that more treasure and weapons be taken to the secret fort up in the salt marshes. It was better, he said, to play things safe where the Strangers were concerned. But this didn't make him feel any easier.

He sat up longer and longer into the nights that followed, deep in thought. Outside his great chamber a cold wind blew, stiffening the streams and rivers like an old man's joints, and covering the ancient, creaking lands with white snowdrifts.

"Perhaps it means nothing," he said to Boudicca one night as she tried to persuade him to go and get some sleep. "Perhaps life will just go on as it has all these years, since that seems to suit the Strangers so well."

Boudicca could see that Prasutagus didn't really believe this. She tried to cheer him up. "I've heard that the new Caesar has always thought it's a waste of money to keep so many legionaries all the way over here. Maybe he'll summon the Strangers back and they'll leave us for good."

She was dismayed to see Prasutagus shaking his head so sadly. "I've heard that rumour, too," he said. "Remember the scroll that the old Caesar had your father put his mark to? Remember the 'loans' they talked about? Well the Strangers won't leave without taking those 'loans' back with them."

"But those greedy pigs have already claimed half of Icenia!" protested Boudicca. "What more do they want?"

"Exactly," said Prasutagus. "*Half* of Icenia. You think about it. They can't very well take half of the land back with them, can they? No, the one thing you can be sure of is that they won't want the land: they'll want other things."

Boudicca had never considered this before. She had

always assumed the Caesar would just send someone over to live as king in his portion of Icenia. "What sort of things?" she said, feeling an icy chill creep up her spine.

"Well, I suppose anything which they consider has the same worth as the land does. They don't care a robin's song for the soft mists rising from the plains or the beautiful dawns over our sea: they only care about gold and power. I'm worried that if they do decide to take whatever they want, Icenia will be ruined, and with the Strangers gone for good we'll be at the mercy of our neighbours once again."

Boudicca was very upset to hear Prasutagus talk this way. She badly wanted to counter his vision of defeat with a rousing idea of her own. Icenia could raise a great army to fight the Strangers when they came here to steal everything. Then they could go on and fight the Trinovanti, and the Atrebati and the Coritani and all the other stupid tribes.

Prasutagus smiled at her when she told him all of this. "Ah! My dear girl!" he said, stroking her face. "Such spirit! But I'm afraid those days are gone now. That's all in the past."

"No, it isn't," cried Boudicca. "I promise you. You're still the most feared warrior in the whole region! We can be great again." But the truth was that Prasutagus was an old man now. He was tired, his muscles were sagging, his tattoos fading, his moustaches long and straggly and he really didn't need lime to make them white anymore; and, as for that noble head, well it was quite bare now, soft and shiny like a baby's.

"I love you, darling," Boudicca said with great passion. "I will always love you."

Prasutagus kissed her hand "My dear, dear girl," he said, "just to have had these years with you and our wonderful daughters makes me the luckiest man in the whole world."

Boudicca held his sword hand tightly and watched him fondly, as he drifted off to sleep in front of the fire. She stayed like that until the fire had all but died away and the first chill light of morning had begun to creep in through the cracks in the chamber wall.

***

Prasutagus chose a good time to die: just before Cailleach, the Old Crone of Winter, hit the ground with her hammer and turned it hard as cold iron. Who would have thought that such a mighty warrior, whose name was enough to strike terror into the hearts of his enemies; who had left behind him a mountain of mangled corpses, a gulley of blood, a sea of mothers' tears; who would have thought that such a one as he would have met with death so peacefully, sitting in front of his hearth, with his beloved wife close beside him?

It was the custom of our people at that time to weep at a birth and to laugh at a death, but Boudicca didn't feel like laughing. When Cara came looking for her at first light, she clung to her friend and the tears ran down her face.

They buried him on the next hill with some of his great store of treasure, and the people of the Iceni raised a great circle of pure white stones which their ancestors had brought back from a raid on the Briganti many years ago.

Then they went back into the fort and gathered about the fires and they waited. They waited for the Strangers to come and claim what was now rightly theirs.

CHAPTER 6
Time-of-ice
February, 60CE

"It didn't take long. A fortnight after the death of Prasutagus, a centuria arrived at the hill fort accompanying a little round Stranger with a chest of scrolls. He had come, he said, under the order of Procurator Decianus Catus. The Procurator was in charge of all the finances of the Province Britannia, and he had ordered that an inventory be made of everything the Iceni possessed.

"Under the Law of Rome," the little chief delegate declared pompously, "it is an offence to make any bequests over that which is due to Caesar." Not for the first time Boudicca wished that she had bothered to learn the Strangers' tongue; she had no idea what this twit was going on about.

Boudicca drew herself up to her full height, which meant that she towered over the short, fat chief delegate. "Look here," she informed him in her most formidable voice, "we had an agreement: half the kingdom belongs to the Caesar, and the other half belongs to me and my daughters."

But the official completely ignored her. He walked about the hill-fort making endless lists of everything he found there. Then he stood by as the legionaries began to help themselves to anything that wasn't rooted to the ground.

"What's going on here?" demanded Boudicca. "You can't take that, put it down immediately. You're only entitled to half!"

The chief delegate put his hand up right in front of her face. "Everything is now forfeit to the Caesar," he said flatly.

"Everything?" exploded Boudicca. "Oh, no, I don't think so. I think there's been some mistake."

"No mistake," said the official.

The Druids started up their terrible wailing, bringing down a million curses on the heads of the Strangers, but the soldiers just pushed them roughly aside and even ran a couple of them through with their swords.

The imprecations of the Druids, however, brought courage to the Iceni warriors, who now came whooping through the enclosure, daubed in war-paint, and began to fight the soldiers. Aesunos managed to kill one legionary who was helping himself to the winter grain store. It was a magnificent gesture, the first of many over that week, but just like all the rest, it was in vain. As Aesunos stepped away from his victim, cheering, another legionary came up behind him with his sword raised and in another instant Aesunos's head was rolling across the ground.

Seeing the death of his comrade, Saenuvax dashed across and thrust his spear into the side of the legionary, but no sooner had he heard the satisfying squelch of its metal tip penetrating flesh and bone, than another soldier charged at him, hacking off his spear-bearing arm at the shoulder.

For the next few days the Strangers came in great numbers to every corner of Icenia. They pulled people from their dwellings, rounded up cattle, removed caskets of treasure; they even tore away the gold torcs which the warriors wore around their necks. Anything that was worthless to them they burned, and they killed anyone who tried to stop them.

Then they gathered up all the slaves, chained them together and forced them to help carry off the plundered goods. The Strangers even took some of the Iceni away with them, knowing that it was a matter of great shame to our people to be enslaved.

Boudicca pleaded with the soldiers not to take Cara.

"Here, take my jewels," she beseeched the soldier who stood by the line of weeping people.

Cara, with a great linking chain around her waist joining her to the other slaves, implored Boudicca piteously. "Don't let them take me, lady, please, please don't let them take me. I want to stay with you!"

"Look, they're gold! Real gold," said Boudicca increasingly

desperate, tugging the rings off her fingers. "Please let her go. She's not a slave. She's my friend. Please, please, you've got to let her go."

The legionary snatched the gold rings from Boudicca's hand and tucked them away in his belt. Then, with a horrible grin on his face, he raised his whip hand and urged the line of slaves, including Cara, out of the enclosure.

Boudicca, Ardra and Briana clung to each other, weeping bitterly as Cara was led away in a great train of slaves, cattle and treasure. All around them were scenes of devastation and ruin. The glow from a hundred burning settlements illuminated the night sky, and the acrid smell of smoke and burning flesh hung in the air. In just a few short days Boudicca had lost everything, but she refused to allow herself to give way to despair for too long. She summoned what remained of the tribe and told them to go into the forests and bring back whatever food they could find. It was the dead of winter, and there wouldn't be much, but no good at all would come from sitting around looking into empty grain-stores and animal stalls.

Then she went to the Druids and poured a libation to the goddess Andraste, as thanks for sparing her beloved daughters. It made her feel stronger to think that the gods were on her side, and she knew that she would need great strength in the time to come. As she prayed, she remembered the night when the Caesar and her father had put their marks to the scroll, and she recalled her own encounter afterwards with the Augury, and the terrible image of the future which had so haunted her.

Summer without flowers; cattle without milk; warriors without courage; sea without fish; woods without trees; people without a king.

People without a king, Queen Boudicca repeated to herself. People without a king. And why, she asked herself, is that such a bad thing? The people have a queen, now; a queen who was raised from girlhood to be a warrior! And two princesses, whose veins run with the blood of two great kings!

The next day, another delegation of Strangers arrived at the ruined fort. They had, they said, come for Queen Boudicca.

She was terrified, but she managed to hide it well. She made the soldiers wait while she dressed as well as she could in what remained of her finery, and then she selected some of the tribe, including Finian the Bard, to go with her as a retinue. Reasoning that she was probably going to be taken into slavery, Boudicca also took the precaution of hiding a phial of liquid hemlock bane in her belt.

"I would rather die than be enslaved," she explained to her daughters. "And I advise you to do the same, girls, should the Strangers try and carry you off."

Ardra was very frightened: she threw her arms around her mother and begged her not to go, but bold Briana stepped forward and gently pulled her sister away.

"Don't worry, mother," the girl said in her clear strong voice. "You go and deal with the Strangers: Ardra and I will govern the kingdom wisely until you return." Then the remaining Iceni warriors stepped forward, forming a protective ring around the two young princesses while Boudicca and her small party were led out of the hill fort.

When they arrived at the council rooms in Camulodunum, Boudicca recognised at once the scroll which the Caesar had tricked her father into putting his mark upon all those years ago. The Procurator Decianus Catus had it spread out before him on a large table and he was tapping it impatiently with a thick finger. He leaned forward on his great fat hairy knuckles, glaring at Boudicca as she entered the room.

"Who is in charge here?" demanded the Procurator. One of his attendants stepped forward and whispered something in his ear. "Well, I haven't come all the way from Londinium for this nonsense," he shouted, "what a waste of my time!" He cast a look of pure disgust in Boudicca's direction. "Get this wild woman out of here! I'm a busy man, you know!"

Boudicca smiled at the Procurator, and politely asked him if he would hear her.

He grunted.

"You see," she began, speaking very slowly, "there's clearly been some sort of mistake. If you look closely at this scroll, you'll see that my father, King Antedios, made an agreement with the Caesar."

The Procurator was looking her up and down with a half-smile about his lips. It was not a friendly smile, and seeing it, Boudicca wondered what sort of people these Strangers were who could turn a smile into a sort of threat.

"I really don't have time for this nonsense," snarled the Procurator at the other officials. "I am here on the Emperor Nero's business and I need to know who's in charge here!"

Finian stepped forward. "This is our Queen, Boudicca," he said in the Strangers' own tongue, "and she speaks for the Iceni tribe."

The Procurator spat his words at the young bard. "Are you serious? I can't discuss the Emperor's business with a woman," he repeated. "Especially such an ugly one."

Oh, she wanted so badly to hurl herself at the rude

Procurator and tear his eyes from his head for his insolence. But instead Boudicca whispered to Finian that perhaps he ought to speak on behalf of the tribe. "After all, you can talk their horrible language," she reasoned sensibly.

Finian relayed the gist of the conversation which followed to Boudicca: it didn't take long. The new Caesar wanted the loans repaid immediately and in full. "Only, of course," the Procurator drawled, "the loans no longer have the same value as they had all those years ago. No: they're worth far more now, and the difference must also be paid – immediately."

Finian stood helplessly before an astonished Boudicca. "What do you want me to tell them?" he asked.

Boudicca gathered her wits. Her first thought was for the secret fort and all the weapons and treasure hidden there. She could, she supposed, just hand it over and maybe then they'd go away. But she knew better than that. It was all the Iceni had now, and the rotten Strangers must never get their filthy hands on it.

Boudicca tossed her hair. "Tell them to get lost," she said. "By the mighty Andraste! They've got some nerve! They take everything we have and then they want more. Well, there's nothing left for them; they've had it all. Tell them that."

Nervously, Finian relayed the Queen's defiant words to the Procurator. When he had heard them, the official turned to look at Boudicca. This time he was not smiling.

"I'm not a fool," he said coldly. "I've done the sums.

When the Divine Claudius first made his agreement with Antedios, he had an inventory made of everything the Iceni owned: the inventory my official took the other day shows a discrepancy of a considerable size. Where's the rest of the treasure?"

Boudicca stood her ground. She met Decianus Catus's stony gaze with one every bit as implacable.

"Take her away," growled the Procurator, keeping his eye on Boudicca all the while. Then he turned to Finian. "You can go back to Icenia and let it be known that the whole land and every living creature within it is now the property of Rome and the Emperor Nero! And if anyone feels like telling me where the rest of the treasure is, I might let them live in return."

Finian's heart was pounding, and the rest of the Iceni delegation groaned in terror as their Queen was led away by the Strangers, but if Boudicca was feeling any fear she certainly didn't let anyone know. She shouted, punched, kicked, spat and swore. "You rotten pigs!" she shrieked, "you filthy, lying, cheating pigs! You ugly, stinking, thieving pigs!" And then one of the guards stepped forward to smack her across the face and everything went black.

***

The pain of the whip lashes had not been the worst of the punishment. She told herself she would happily bear a

106

thousand times more pain if it would help to save her people
and her lands from the scourge of defeat and humiliation.

I shall not be killed.
I shall not be hunted.
I shall not be captive;
I shall not be wounded.
Neither fire, nor sun, nor moon shall burn me.
Neither lake, nor river, nor sea shall drown me.

She had repeated the song over and again as the soldiers
had beaten her. And at every lash she had dreamt of
vengeance. And that was long before she reached the fort
and discovered what they had done to her beloved
daughters.

As soon as Boudicca had left for Camulodunum, the
Strangers had returned to her fort. At first it was assumed
that they had come to take the Princesses away with them,
and the warriors set to defend them fought very bravely: a
few of them even died in the struggle. However, the
Strangers had not come to steal the girls; they had come to
do something even worse. They had come to break their
spirit, in the hope that the girls would tell them where the
rest of the Iceni treasure was hidden.

It was a mean and cowardly thing to do, but the
Strangers believed that hurting the princesses would prove
to the rest of the tribe that they were now properly in charge.

When Boudicca returned the next day, it seemed as though everyone had vanished in to the mist covering the plains. As soon as it was safe, she made her own way across the salt marshes, to the secret fort.

Ardra was sitting huddled in a corner refusing to look at anyone other than her sister, and weeping all the time. She had not eaten since it had happened, and was looking even more pale and delicate than usual. This was bad enough for any mother to bear, but when Boudicca saw her beautiful, bold Briana, she felt her heart crack like ice on a river.

The girl had such a wild look to her eyes, her hair was all over the place and she was raving at everyone and everything. Ardra had ran straightway to her mother's arms, and was clinging to her sobbing inconsolably, but Briana just stood rigid before Boudicca, a terrible darkness covering her features.

"What are we going to do to them, mother?" she shrieked. "How many deaths can we make them die? How many? How many?" Her sister's terrible rage only made Ardra shake and cry even more.

For the first time since Prasutagus's death, Queen Boudicca felt her strength leave her: she couldn't stop herself from falling to the ground. Clasping Ardra to her, she howled like a she-wolf caught in a trap. She howled and she howled, and yet no tears came.

CHAPTER 7
Time-of-the-winds
March, 60CE

❝ The Trinovanti Chieftain was no more than a kid, younger than Princess Briana. He wasn't nearly as tall as Boudicca. Still, he was doing his best to look the part of a brave Trinovanti warrior of old: his muscles stood out like plum stones beneath his tattooed skin and his lime-caked hair stood up in stiff peaks.

The young man had just finished telling the Queen all about how great he was on the battlefield, but Boudicca knew full well that this was just big talk. He was so young he could only have known life under the Strangers, and that meant he wouldn't have had a chance to practise his fighting skills on anyone apart from his little brother.

"Still," she thought, "beggars can't be choosers." Ever since taking refuge in the secret fort, Boudicca had thought of nothing else but destroying the colony of Strangers based at Camulodunum, but she couldn't do it on her own: she was going to need help. The earnest young man standing before her didn't look like much, but he was going to have to do, for the time being.

He was a kinsman of Finian the Bard, part of a small mob of restless Trinovanti boys who spent their time causing trouble and, although he didn't know it yet, he was going to help to persuade the rest of his tribe to join the Iceni and kick out the Strangers.

Boudicca sniffed. "If you're so tough," she said, "how come you let the Strangers run everything in Trinovantes?"

The young Chieftain looked hurt, his youthful pride easily wounded. "Oh, that's just our parents and grandparents," he bristled. "They're all too old and stupid to fight; but all of us Trinovanti kids really hate the Strangers and we're ready to take them on."

Boudicca sighed. It was going to take more than a few stone-chucking hooligans to push the Strangers out of the Yellow and Red Lands.

"I dare say," she continued, picking idly on a rabbit bone, which was all any of them had had to eat for days, "that a lot of Trinovanti have got used to the lifestyle, now; they've all got nice jobs working in the fort and the temple down in Camulodunum, and from what I've heard the money's not bad either."

"Well, they do grumble about the taxes!" declared the young Chieftain.

Boudicca yawned and threw the rabbit bone onto the fire. "Mmmm. The thing is: are they prepared to go to war over it?" she asked.

The Chieftain gulped. "War?" he stammered. "What, you mean with the Strangers?"

Boudicca fixed him with her most formidable expression. "Or are you all so happy with the way things are down there in the Red Lands that you don't really care about being slaves?" She laughed a hard, bitter-edged little laugh. "King Prasutagus was right: the Trinovanti are cowardly, creeping slugs. He always said your ancestors went about with their heads hung low out of pure shame."

The boy was really upset to hear this. "He said what? Well, that's rubbish! The Trinovanti are great! We have the courage of lions and we don't fear anything!"

"Well, then how come the minute you saw the Strangers walking into Camulodunum you all just threw down your weapons and ran towards them with trays of cakes?"

"We did no such thing!" he whined.

Boudicca shrugged, "Well, that's what I heard."

The young Chieftain looked crushed.

"Look," said Boudicca in a more conciliatory tone of voice. "I don't really blame you. We used to feel the same way about the Strangers here. We thought they were alright, and as long as they didn't bother us too much, we had a good life, with plenty of everything. But then one day, it all changed," Boudicca reached up and snapped her fingers right in his face: "just like that."

Boudicca jumped up, her eyes flashing dangerously now. "You might think that you're all perfectly happy down there in the Red Lands, crouching in slavery, but let me tell you, one day the Strangers will come to your fort and they'll take away all your slaves and cattle, and –" She broke off, so angry she could hardly speak. "Look at this," she said, pulling down her tunic to reveal the six, angry red wheals extending across the width of her back. "Look at it! The Strangers did that to me, and one day they'll do it to your mother or your sister or your girlfriend too. Or they'll do worse: like they did to my daughters!"

The young Chieftain was too ashamed to look at her. He was looking down at the floor. "We're not allowed to be men any more," he said, his voice husky with emotion, "the Strangers have taken even that away from us."

Boudicca lifted his chin up and looked into his eyes. "Then join me and fight them," she said quietly. "Chase them from these lands; force them back beyond the ninth wave." Her eyes glinted. In an instant the boy knew that he would fight to the death for her.

"I'll come back here tomorrow," he said, "with as many people as I can find who hate the Strangers as much as I do. You talk to them: tell them what you've just told me. I know they'll want to help. The Trinovanti are not cowards. We're as brave as any other tribe in these lands."

"I know," said Boudicca. "The Strangers have cast a spell

over us all. They put the whole region to sleep. Well, now it's time to wake up!".

A few days later, Boudicca addressed a huge crowd of Iceni and Trinovanti: "Have you ever noticed how exposed the strangers' settlement at Camulodunum is?" she asked. "Oh, it's quite splendid, with its wide, straight streets and its enormous statues. But have you ever asked yourself: where are the fortifications? Where are the mighty palisades? And have you ever considered how the settlement is occupied by old men and guarded by – why, as you have told yourselves – lazy and corrupt so-called soldiers?"

A burly warrior standing at the back of the gathering called out to her. "What would you have us do, lady? They've taken away our weapons. We can't fight the Strangers with words and pots and pans!" His friends started laughing.

"You men have allowed our land to become over-run with vermin," Boudicca went on. "Because that's what the Strangers are: filth, filth! What are we going to leave for our children? A field of withered crops, that's all. A pigsty, filled with the dirt and stink of the Strangers!"

Boudicca signalled to the young Chieftain and his friends. A few minutes later, they re-entered the hall bearing piles of shields and spears and swords, which they laid down in front of the fire. The glare of the metal lit up the dark hall, dazzling the astonished crowd.

"Long ago my husband, the mighty King Prasutagus –

may the gods protect his spirit – asked the Trinovanti to help us enter the fort at Camulodunum so we could steal weapons from the Strangers. He had those weapons, together with a stock of our own brought here, to this secret place, as a precaution against the day when the Strangers proved themselves enemies of the Iceni and our neighbours, the brave people of the Red Lands. Well, that day has come!" Boudicca stepped forward and picked up a spear from the top of the pile, grasping it in her right hand; then she took aim, and swept her powerful arm across the crowd. Some of the people ducked instinctively, but others recognised the ancient challenge; they stood straight and met her gaze unflinchingly as the spear point passed within inches of their faces.

"If you have forgotten the songs of glory and victory our ancestors taught to us," Boudicca was saying, "I have not. I hear them all around me. Our ancestors are berating us; our children are beseeching us. They are telling me to destroy Camulodunum: to soak its streets with the blood of the Strangers!"

The room was utterly silent. Nobody moved. Then an old woman stepped forward. "Give me a spear!" she cried. "I will kill a Stranger for you, lady."

Wild shrieks and howls rang out as the people fell upon the weapons; the battle frenzy continued well into the night, and was still going strong at first light, as the people followed Boudicca, with Ardra and Briana at her side, towards Camulodunum.

CHAPTER 8
Time-of-brightness
The Sacred Grove, Mona {Anglesey},
May, 60CE

❝ Whenever he was on campaign, Suetonius Paulinus, fourth Governor of the Province of Britannia, was in the habit of looking up at the sky each morning as he stepped out of his tent. He did this without fail, even though he knew without looking that the skies would be grey and full of rain clouds. As far as he was concerned it was always raining in Britannia.

He had been in the Pale Lands since the beginning of the year, the coldest, dampest part of the whole gloomy Province; he could scarcely remember the last time the sun had warmed his back.

"By the mighty Jove!" the Governor muttered to himself, "how I hate this rotten country. I wish I could be in Amalfi right now, with the sun shining on my face and a goblet of good wine in my hand."

He had long ago decided that the dreadful weather was the reason why the natives were so moody and difficult. They're a miserable lot! Ignorant savages! They've never shown the slightest appreciation for all the great gifts of civilisation which we have bestowed upon them.

As far as Suetonius Paulinus was concerned, it was no bad thing that the Emperor Nero had decided it was time to get tough on the natives of Britannia; he had always thought that Emperor Claudius had been much too soft on the barbarians. Mind you, there was the odd occasion when the new Emperor went too far. After all, if you step too hard on a pomegranate, what happens? Suetonius Paulinus slipped his boot off and, with a muttered curse, scraped the mud from the underside of his foot. Well, in general you have nothing but a sticky mess to wipe away.

Of course, it was no good trying to explain any of that to the Emperor Nero: sitting all those miles away in glorious, sunny Rome. He had absolutely no idea what it was like for Suetonius Paulinus stuck in Britannia. He only kept the Province going because he believed all those old stories about piles of gleaming gold in the mountains.

Well, Suetonius Paulinus knew nothing about any gold, nor did he care much; as far as he was concerned, especially on his more dispirited days, the entire enterprise was a waste of time and money.

The invasion force, made up of the splendid men of the

XIVth and XXth Legions, was already lined up awaiting his inspection as Suetonius Paulinus reached the seashore. They were preparing to invade the sacred forest of the Druids on the little island known as Mona. The island lay just off the western edge of Britannia in uncertain waters, which like everything else about this crazy place followed no pattern or rule, going from really shallow to very deep in the space of a few cubita. After investigating the waters they were now preparing to cross, they had decided that the foot soldiers would need to make some flat-bottomed vessels for themselves, and the cavalry could ford the shallows, dismounting to swim alongside their horses in the depths.

Of course, crossing the water was only the beginning. As to what they would find when they reached the other side – well! Like all of his men, the governor had heard the lurid tales brought back by Julius Caesar over one hundred years before, of a ghastly temple in the heart of the thick forest, where the sun never shone, and the trees were sprayed with human blood. There the barbaric gods were appeased with hideous offerings. The priests were half-man and half-god, apparently, and guarded by a bunch of women, winged like the Furies, with writhing serpents for hair, who could tear a man's heart from his chest with their bare hands.

The legionaries were quieter than usual as they set sail, paddling silently towards an unknown fate.

Soon Suetonius Paulinus could make out the opposite shore of the isle of Mona. He could see a dense throng of native warriors, a mêlée of blue body paint and white stiffened hair, each one naked as the day he was born, even though it was freezing cold.

As he got nearer, the governor heard the wail of what he took to be some wild beast. The eerie noise sent a shudder through him. On the shore wild women were running about the warriors, shrieking horribly to their gods for protection. Behind this hideous spectacle, it was just possible to catch a glimpse of the Druids, in their long white gowns. They had their hands uplifted to the heavens as if invoking the gods to bring down the sky.

Suetonius Paulinus didn't scare easily, but he caught himself swallowing hard and, just for a moment, he felt his legs tremble in the icy water. When he reached the shore he looked back over his shoulder at his men standing openmouthed and motionless in the water, making no effort to draw their weapons or clamber on to land.

The governor heard his own voice roaring at them: "Are you men? Are you afraid of a bunch of crazy women? Have you forgotten that you're Romans?"

He felt a palpable relief when his declamations were joined by those of his officers; in another breath, the men of the IXth Legion were running past him up the beach, their standards billowing in the sea-breeze; and then they were at work on the edge of the forest: stabbing, thrusting, slashing in all directions; wrapping the enemy in the flames of their own fire-brands.

It didn't take long to destroy the sacred groves. The axe-men went to work while the battle was still raging. The warriors met death unflinchingly, but they met it all the same. The Druids, unarmed, fell like the trees to which they clung. Soon the ground was thick with the mulch of blood and bones and brains.

Suetonius Paulinus had just finished praising the men of the XIVth and XXth Legions for their courage when he received the tidings. The so-called Queen Boudicca of the Iceni had gone on a violent rampage, along with up to 200,000 barbarians: Camulodunum was already in ruins, and now she was heading towards Londinium.

CHAPTER 9
Time-of-brightness
Boudicca's camp, outside Camulodunum
May, 60CE

❝ The Strangers took it as a bad sign when the great statue of Victory in Camulodunum suddenly toppled from its plinth and lay face down on the ground. It was the first inkling they had that something really bad was about to happen. Those who had the gift of foresight ran about proclaiming that this was an omen: "Camulodunum is going to fall," they said, "just as the statue has done."

Plenty of people were quick to dismiss this sort of talk as nothing more than superstitious fear-mongering, but when, during a meeting in the council chamber the next day, a great noise was heard by everyone it became a little harder to be quite so dismissive. The noise was something like the roar of a mighty crowd and it was so loud that some of the Strangers ran outside, fully expecting to see a great commotion on the streets. But there was nothing more than a few farmers and their sheep ambling along in the afternoon sunshine.

The next omen came that very evening. A group of terrified Trinovanti workers came running into the square; they claimed to have heard strange groans and howls, the sort of thing a terrible, savage beast might make, echoing around the empty amphitheatre as they swept away the blood-stained sawdust from the arena after a bull-fight.

Then the very next morning a group of Trinovanti fishermen turned up at the market with an even stranger story. They said that, as they had drawn their nets from the mouth of the river Thamesis, they'd noticed how the water beneath their boat suddenly became cloudy. When they peered over the edge of their boat into the depths of the river, the cloudiness gave way to the image of a colony in ruins. As the strange vision faded, the water had turned the colour of blood, right before their eyes.

Well, after this incredible run of events, even the most sceptical among the Strangers began to feel anxious. The veteran legionaries who were garrisoned at Camulodunum's mighty fort decided the best thing to do would be to send a desperate message to the Procurator Catus Decianus back in Londinium, asking him to send them reinforcements.

A day later the Procurator wrote back to say that, while their worries seemed a bit premature, he would send them all the men he could spare: two centuria of a hundred men each.

***

Boudicca was delighted when she heard of the growing fear and uneasiness in the doomed settlement of Camulodunum. At a mighty feast in her forest camp, overlooking the town, she congratulated the Trinovanti amphitheatre workers and the fishermen for their great skill as Bards; then she paid tribute to some of the native inhabitants of Camulodunum, the men who had succeeded in pulling over the statue in the dead of night without being detected.

As she joined all of her followers in laughing heartily at the stupidity of the Strangers, Boudicca was especially pleased to see Ardra join in the fun: the fishermen's tale had been her idea, and everyone had been most impressed to see such a young girl demonstrate such great story-telling skill. During the feast, Finian the Bard had made a special effort to tell the princess how nice it was to see her smiling for once, and how pretty she looked.

But this was really Boudicca's celebration. She had swept out of the secret fort in the salt marsh with little more than a thousand followers, and now as they reached their destination of Camulodunum, the number had swelled thirty fold. Angry Britons, be they Iceni, Trinovanti and even

Catevallauni, had all flocked to join her, roused by her great, passionate speeches and the story of what the Strangers had done to the princesses.

Boudicca had felt many things the past few weeks: rage and pain and sorrow, but now it was time to feel pride. She missed Prasutagus, of course, especially his strong arms around her in the night; she missed Cara, who had always understood her better than she did herself. Sometimes, the thought of all that she had lost threatened to overwhelm her, but just now she could feel the swell of satisfaction in her bosom.

"Mother, when are we going to do more than just play foolish tricks upon the Strangers?" Briana's once snow-white face was flushed with anger.

"It's been two weeks since we started the rebellion and we haven't spilt a single drop of their disgusting blood."

Boudicca sighed. "Oh, Briana, just try and enjoy the party! You really are the most impatient girl!" Boudicca loved Briana so much, and she longed to hold the girl close to her, but she knew from experience that she would just push her away. "You know full well that we have to wait for a sign," she continued, trying not to sound so cross. Boudicca glanced over at the Druids who had been sitting hunched over a dead raven all day. "We can't do anything unless it's well-starred. All things happen in their own time, you'll see."

But Briana was having none of it. "What's wrong with

now?" she bawled. "You've heard the intelligence. There are only 10,000 decrepit old soldiers left holding the fort with a few paltry reinforcements. The Governor is far away, and with him the best of the Legions. The Trinovanti civilians will join us at the first hint of trouble."

"Briana, that's enough!" said Boudicca severely. "You're barely seventeen! I've been a Queen for twenty years, and before that I was a warrior princess when that meant something!"

Briana scowled at her mother. "If you've been around so long, you ought to have learned a few things by now," she sneered.

"You've no idea what you're talking about!" exclaimed Boudicca.

"Yes I do," yelled Briana. "I know that grandfather let the Strangers walk in here and take over as he was too cowardly to fight them; and I know that father let him. Perhaps if you hadn't just let men tell you what to do all the time, you'd have been a better mother to me and Ardra, and we wouldn't have had such a horrible time!" Briana's eyes were cold, and Boudicca couldn't bear to look at them a moment longer.

"How can you say such dreadful things?" Boudicca shouted. "Your father was a brave man, and a good, wise king. It's not his fault that the Strangers live by a different code to us. I won't have you talking in this way about things you know nothing about. I've always put you girls first, ahead of everything. Go! Go! Out of my sight."

"I don't care what you say! I'm an Iceni! We live for glory!" screamed Briana. "We can't creep about like worms in the soil our ancestors bequeathed to us, while the Strangers trample us underfoot!"

Boudicca was shocked to see such passion erupt from her eldest daughter. "By Andraste," she thought, "she will be a great Queen; but will she ever know peace?"

***

The Strangers who ran things in the colony of Camulodunum, along with the veterans and the few guards sent from Londinium to defend them, decided to move into the temple while they awaited the arrival of the rebel forces. It was the only building in the whole settlement which was well fortified, and they thought they would be safe there. But the councillors and veterans of Camulodunum had underestimated the secret enemies in their midst.

The Strangers told the native Trinovanti living and working in Camulodunum to build a protective ditch around the town, but the people made up excuses about the weather; they dug in the parts where the ditch was sure to fill with water, and then they deliberately broke their tools. Next the Strangers commanded the enslaved Trinovanti to throw up a palisade around the garrison; but the workers dug the pits so shallowly that the tree trunks they placed in them toppled over at the slightest impact.

And all the while the Trinovanti kept Boudicca fully informed of their ruses and of everything else that happened in the town. They told her where the guards were positioned in the garrison and the exact location of the weapon stores: they told her how she could get her hands on the supplies set aside for the now inevitable siege, and they peed in the water stores.

Boudicca and her great army encircled Camulodunum like wolves around a sheep pen. And then, before giving the order to advance, Boudicca made a great speech.

"Listen to me," she commanded the excited hordes, "you all know the difference between being free and being a slave. The Strangers robbed us of our riches; they make us pay taxes; they make us work on our own land for nothing and take away everything that we grow. Well, I would rather die in battle than live like this!" Boudicca paused here to look across at her daughters: Ardra was smiling at her, but Briana was still angry.

"The Strangers are looking down on us; they're crushing us," she said, glancing once more at Briana "as though we had no more right to live than worms!"

A holler, a yelp, a terrifying cacophony: it carried on throughout the whole day and through the night, and all through the next day and all through the next night. It was as though, having been compelled to be silent for so long, the people were now resolved to never be silent again. The terrified Strangers barricaded in the temple managed to hold out for two days, but then they too, like all of the surrounding region, were engulfed by the murderous rebels.

The IXth Legion Hispana was more than 80 miles away when the news reached them. They came as quickly as they could to help the citizens of Camulodunum in the desperate battle, but the rebels were waiting for them on the road. Every last infantryman was mercilessly rooted out and cut down, and the commander himself only just managed to flee with some of his cavalry, back to his entrenchments in the Black Lands.

The jubilant rebels watched him run away, and then, with Boudicca in the vanguard, wheeled round and headed south: towards the settlement of Londinium.

CHAPTER 10
Time-of-brightness
Londinium,
May, 60CE

❝Suetonius Paulinus and his Legion reached Londinium just ahead of the rebels, after a 250-mile march. He was relieved to find the settlement still standing, and to find himself looking down from a hilltop on to a small maze of streets edged with farmland, and with a silver rope of river twisting through it like a great eel.

"That miserable coward, Procurator Catus Decianus, is even less of a man than I took him for," he was telling the tribune who had escorted him on the reconnaissance mission. "Perhaps if he had thought less of his own status and wealth and applied himself more to the task of government he wouldn't have had to go running squealing like a stuck hog across the sea to Gaul. Well, we're better off without him. There's been nothing

128

but trouble since he took over."

The tribune was young and very ambitious, and he liked being in the confidence of the powerful Legate, the Governor of the whole province; however, he was aware that these were dangerous times, and the Emperor Nero had spies everywhere. He didn't want to do or say anything which might halt his progress through the ranks: it was even possible that the Legate was setting him some sort of a test of his loyalty. "Oh. I'm sure that the Procurator acted with the best intentions," he said at last.

Paulinus looked at the young tribune quizzically. "Really?" he said, raising his eyebrows in mock surprise. "And what do you suppose he hoped to achieve by running away after stuffing as much treasure as he could carry in his toga, leaving the province without any administration at a time of crisis?"

The tribune blushed. He should have known that Suetonius Paulinus was too much a soldier to be taken in by any misjudged cleverness.

"I suppose it matters little, in the scheme of things," the Governor said, looking back towards the town. "It's not as if Londinium is a great colony, after all. It's full of merchants, and has no fortifications to speak of." He sighed, feeling a flicker of disappointment. He had hurried here hoping to do battle, but he could see now that there was little chance of that. Perhaps that was a blessing.

"We can muster how many?" he asked the tribune.

"About five hundred, maybe more, maybe less..."

Suetonius scratched his chin and thought for a few moments. From here it was possible to see almost every street and narrow lane; there was nothing at all between these hills and the settlement itself.

"Well," said Suetonius, "I have no desire to suffer the same fate as the IXth Legion Hispana." His horse stirred impatiently beneath him. "It's decided then," he said curtly.

"What is?" asked the tribune.

"Well, I'm not about to risk another miserable defeat at the hands of the barbarians; not for somewhere as insignificant as that." Suetonius Paulinus scanned the valley once more. "No, we'll be better off concentrating our efforts and resources on building a proper defence so that we can secure the rest of the province."

The tribune was shocked. "But we can't just leave them, there's more than 30,000 people living down there: Roman people!"

"Oh, and I dare say they won't be at all happy about it. They'll weep and beg, beat their breasts and tear their garments, but there's no two ways about it: we're going to have to withdraw the post. Let them know that we'll take under our banner any one who can take their place in the column," the Legate was saying as he steered his horse back towards the road. "As for the others, they'll have to trust to the gods." He glanced over his shoulder at the dumbfounded tribune. "That's right, my friend," he said with a smile. "Leadership is a heavy burden. Some might even say that it is a curse."

***

It was as if one hundred thousand devils descended on Londinium that night, and when it was all over Boudicca could scarcely believe that it had happened. Flames lapped at the side of every building and gave to the surroundings a livid hue, suddenly illuminating one scene of horror after another before casting it back into darkness once more.

Any of the Roman citizens of Londinium who were fit for war had left with Suetonius Paulinus before Boudicca arrived, but there were still many left behind: women, children, the aged and infirm, and those who, inexplicably, loved life in that drab valley so much they couldn't bring themselves to leave it. Those poor people wept openly to see their settlement burning; they ran about in desperation, with buckets of water trying to save it. Some of them threw themselves and their children headlong into their beloved river to escape death at the hands of the rebels.

Boudicca saw many terrible things that night, which she knew she would never be able to forget, but her heart only stopped once: when she saw Briana run screaming through the streets, her spear dripping with blood, her hair wild and loose, stabbing indiscriminately at all who crossed her path. Boudicca knew that she should be proud of the brave warrior spirit that had possessed her daughter, but it made her sad to think that the sweet little girl, whom she had once rocked to sleep, was gone forever. "That baby," thought Boudicca, "drank in vengeance with every sup of my milk. Maybe that's the problem. After all, she's heard me talk every day of her life about driving the Strangers from these lands."

By the next morning, as the rebels prepared to leave Londinium, nothing remained of the city but a smouldering layer of dark clay, and the butchered remains of the citizens, many of them impaled on skewers, their sightless eyes looking down on to the razed buildings and streets.

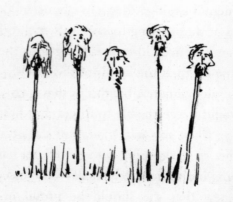

Boudicca was feeling tired. She wandered down to the river and scooped up a handful of water to wash her face and as she did so caught her reflection. What a mess: her hair was singed and dirty, and her face twisted and wrought into something hard and lined. She looked old.

"Prasutagus was right," she thought. "War is horrible, even when you're winning. It's much better to live in peace and comfort." Boudicca shivered. "Still, we don't have a choice right now. Those days will never come again until the last drop of blood from the last Stranger left here has been shed on the soil of this poor broken land."

She was, you see, as hard as the earth she came from, and, like all her tribe, she was afraid of nothing.

***

Suetonius Paulinus had spent most of his life at war and there was very little that could shock him, but the descriptions of what the rebels had done to Londinium came close to making his blood freeze.

After leaving Londonium, Boudicca and the rebel army had turned northwest and were now encircling Verulamium, a colony a little bit smaller than Camulodunum, whose native population consisted mostly of what remained of the Catevallauni.

"Leave them to their fate," had been the Legate Suetonius Paulinus's first instinct when he heard the news.

Like Londinium, the colony was not strategically important, and most of the Roman citizens had already fled. What was more, in spite of an urgent summons, the nearest troops, the IInd Legion Augusta, had failed to arrive, and now it would be difficult to gather enough of a force at such short notice. The time must be right, he thought to himself, to meet these barbarians in a decisive battle: one which we cannot lose. We must show the world that we are not afraid of Boudicca and her rabble.

"These barbarians are not soldiers," he told the tribune, "they're ill-disciplined swine who despise all the laws of war. They attack only the weak and feeble and all they want to do is spill blood and plunder and loot. Let them drink themselves into a stupor, and when they're sleeping it off, we'll be ready for them."

"But noble Legate," the young tribune was keen to demonstrate his own ability to think dispassionately. "Won't the native people of Verulamium join the rebels? Our intelligence says that there's already almost 200,000 of them."

Suetonius rubbed his chin impatiently. "First rule of combat," he barked at the tribune. "Know the enemy! I have spent longer than I care to think in this pit. I have fought with these savages more times than you've shaved. They might hate us, but they hate each other even more. Never forget, we were invited here by the neighbours of the Catevallauni who were sick of the way the old King

Cunobelin and his sons, Prince Caradoc and Togodumnus, were running about the place stealing whatever they could put their hands on." The tribune looked surprised. "Oh yes, they welcomed us in when they thought we might help them protect their sheep and mud huts from their neighbours."

"I had no idea."

"Well, you should: divide and rule, you see. That's how it works. That rabble won't welcome the native barbarians of Verulamium into their ranks. They'll kill every last one of them."

Left alone, Suetonius Paulinus made the calculations once more: without the men of the IInd he could muster maybe 10,000 men, no more. Still, they would be some of the best soldiers available to him: men of the XXth and the XIVth, together with whichever auxiliaries were stationed in the region who could be most quickly assembled. Ten thousand of the best Roman soldiers against – how many had the tribune said were now marching with Boudicca? – crazy, shrieking, fearless barbarians.

Suetonius sighed. Ah well, as he always said, in every battle it is the courage of a few which, in the end, wins the day. He closed his eyes and tried to envision the laurel wreath of glory being placed upon his head. If he could see it, it would happen, he told himself. For a moment he was there on the battlefield. He could hear the tribunes shouting at the men, as he had heard so many times before:

"Keep your ranks! Now let fly the javelins! Now advance! Bear down with your bucklers! Hack a bloody path with your swords! Pursue them! Pursue them!"

"Be victorious," he said to nobody in particular, "and you shall have everything."

CHAPTER 11
The Place of the Chariots

Blood and wine and joy!
Blood and wine and joy!
Fire and blood and steel!
Fire and blood and steel!
Oak and earth and sea!
Oak and earth and sea!
Dance and song and death!
Dance and song and death!
Let the sword blades swing!
Let the sword blades swing!
Sing the song of steel!
Sing the song of steel
Blood and wine and joy!
Fire and blood and steel!
Oak and earth and sea!

Dance and song and death!
Yes, dance and song and death!

The atmosphere on the plain that day was like a great feast.
There were fires everywhere and people were singing and
dancing. Those who were either too young or too old to join
in the fighting were sitting in wagons, which they had positioned hoping for a good view of the battle. They were smiling and cheering and waving at the warriors who warmed
up by wrestling with one another.

The Bards were whipping everyone up into a great frenzy of excitement by reciting the great battles of the past,
which were full of lurid descriptions of what had happened
to those ancient enemies. Naturally, this led to some out-
breaks of fighting: when the Iceni Bards sang about how
their ancestors had slaughtered the Trinovanti, for instance;
or the Catuvellauni Bards (for lots of Catuvellauni had
joined the great army at Verulamium) sang rude songs
about the Iceni. However, for the most part, everyone managed to get along, joined together in the task of killing
Strangers.

The battlefield itself was surrounded by dense woods,
and had only one narrow point of entry. By the time
Boudicca arrived there, the Strangers had already taken their
position, up on a ridge overlooking the plain, with the
thickest part of the forest behind them.

Standing aloft in her chariot with the princesses at her

side, Boudicca had a good sight of the enemy almost immediately: a lowering presence on the horizon. The scouts informed her that Suetonius Paulinus appeared to have placed his legions in three tight wedges, with the infantry in the middle and the cavalry on either side. Boudicca could see the arrangement quite clearly, and as she looked up towards the incline, she wondered what it meant.

Briana's eyes were shining as they scanned the neat ranks. "Look mother," she was saying excitedly, "I don't think the Strangers like our noise. It looks like they're shrinking back with terror!" Boudicca looked to where Briana was pointing, but all she could make out were the billowing standards and the plumes of their helmets bobbing in the breeze. She felt Ardra's hand slip into hers.

"They look very neat and tidy, don't they?" she was saying.

Briana groaned. "You don't win battles by being neat and tidy. You win battles by being fearless."

Boudicca closed her eyes and allowed the chaos and noise of the battlefield to overwhelm her. The warriors were defying the gods to strike them down; the women and children were flinging insults at the clouds; the Augury and Wise Women were tearing the skies with their shrill keening; and hundreds of horn-blowers were blasting their carnyxes, the little wooden tongues of the bird-shaped trumpets vibrating wildly.

Boudicca raised her strong white arms and called for silence. Gradually a hush descended upon the multitude, and all eyes turned to her. She swallowed hard and began.

"To me and the daughters of the mighty Prasutagus," she said in her powerful and commanding voice, "this battle is not about recovering our wealth, our kingdom, our power. We may be queens, but we're just like the poorest among you: for we're not free." She faltered for a moment. But Boudicca was never one to be lost for words for long. "Look around you," she continued, her eyes shining, "look around and see how many of you there are, gathered together from all the great tribes of the Red and Yellow Lands! Behold this proud display and carry it in your hearts as you ride into battle! For in this place we must either conquer, or die with glory!" Boudicca paused and a great cheer went up. Everyone went wild again, dancing and shouting and singing and cheering. But before the battle could begin, the Druids were reminding Boudicca that it was necessary to perform one last ritual.

The Augury was crouched upon the ground in front of a small pyre, her bony arms clasped around her knees, squinting up at the clouds looking for a sign that it was time to release the sacred hare, emissary of the goddess Andraste. From the way the beast dashed across the battlefield, the Augury could divine how a battle would go. It was also to be hoped that one of the Strangers, seeing the hare bolt, would instinctively hurl his spear at it: if the hare was struck and died, so would the courage of the enemy.

The Augury traced the plume of smoke from the fire with her outstretched arms, and a hush fell on the assembled masses as the old woman began to wail. Her long white hair swept about her in circles until it seemed to merge with the smoke from the pyre, and her unearthly song filled the sky.

"Give me the hare," Boudicca commanded, her heart pounding so hard she scarcely had breath for the words. "It's time."

All eyes were upon the Queen as she stepped down from the chariot and moved towards the Augury. Even the hare seemed to be aware of the gravity of the moment, and was stone still as she placed it against her breast.

At this point, the Augury suddenly stopped, her head thrown back, her mouth opened in a silent scream, her eyes frozen in terror. Boudicca could tell how it would go even before she set the hare loose.

"So be it," she thought. "I'm not afraid to die." She looked across at her daughters standing at the edge of the plain. "Goodbye my darlings," she whispered, and her heart clenched. In the moments before she released the hare, Boudicca remembered the marshland birds of her homeland. How frail and spindly they were, and yet she had seen those birds rise up against the wild dogs that prowled amongst the thin grasses, and fight to the death. "Be proud!" she cried, her words carried on the breeze to her daughters, "remember, death is only the beginning."

She opened her cloak, and watched as the hare ran from her as fast as the wind.

Then, summoning all her courage, Boudicca turned to face the Strangers. "You are cunning and clever," she thought, "and well-fed and well-armed. But you're afraid of death." She kept her eyes fixed on the blur of grey metal, red plumes and golden standards. "And I am not."

"Let my enemies know," she declared, "that I have all the power of the heavens on my side. All the fire of the sun, all the whiteness of the snows, all the wrath of the lightning that splits the sky in its fury..."

For a fleeting moment she felt her legs tremble as she climbed on board her chariot and took her spear in her hand. As she stood there in the moment before the battle, the wind blew through her long hair, sweeping it across her face and she took the god-sent opportunity to close her eyes. The fate of her daughters was already decided, but Boudicca prayed that they might find shelter, deep in the dark forests, perhaps, or in the Pale Lands where the sun sinks each night into the endless sea at the edge of the world. For she knew that, whatever happened, they would find themselves far away from the wild and misty fens where the reeds wafted in the breeze; far, far away from the flat, horizonless lands of Icenia: her beloved Icenia.

The clamouring began the instant she lifted her spear.

The battle was swift and decisive. In the moments just before Boudicca had let loose the sacred hare, some in her ranks had been alarmed to see Badbh Catha, the Battle Crow, flying above their heads, bleeding and with a rope around its neck. They quaked to see it alight upon the shoulder of one who stood in their midst, a man with one eye, one hand, one leg, and on his back a roast pig, which, though glistening and crisp, was still squealing. It was a horrible portend, yet not one person ran from the field.

Boudicca had four large-chested horses harnessed to her chariot, each one strong enough to wrench the great rocks from the sea; their fine, polished bridles glinting in the light like gems. All through the battle, she kept her grey eyes wide open.

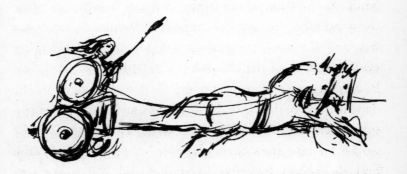

The legions advanced in a close line; but the Britons stood firm with abandoned ferocity. When the legions rushed forward in a wedge-shape, they trapped those brave warriors who had placed themselves at the front: the most reckless, the most eager to kill, were the first to fall. First the auxiliaries, then the cavalry bore down on them, their pikes stabbing at bare heads, at unarmoured backs, at naked arms flung up in self-defence.

Some ran back to defend their families watching in the wagons, but the Strangers pursued them, ruthless to the last. Few were spared.

As soon as the battle began to turn, Briana had sent Ardra into the forest, telling Finian, who was supposed to be recording the battle, to wait with her until it was over. Then she dashed from the wagon, hurling herself into the mêlée armed only with her spear.

Boudicca found Briana on the field, dazed and bloody. She pulled the dying girl into the chariot beside her and urged the horses on into the forest, until sweat like white sea-foam covered their necks. Briana was on the floor of the chariot looking up at her mother, the pain of her wounds made worse by the jolting, yet she never complained.

As they reached a dense part of the forest Boudicca reined the horses in and held Briana in her arms. She smoothed the hair from her daughter's brow and cradled her against her bosom. "Ssshh now, Briana. Soon you will be with father and all your noble ancestors," she told the dying girl.

She kept talking long after Briana could no longer hear her, and she kept kissing her lips long after they had grown cold.

Finian and Ardra found her by the sounds of her sobs.

"You need to get away from here, Lady," the Bard told her. "If the Strangers catch you they'll take you to Rome as their slave."

"No," said Boudicca, "you and Ardra must flee." She handed him the gold torc she had around her neck, her battle jewellery, the only bit of treasure she had removed from the secret fort before she marched off to destroy Camulodunum. "Take it," she commanded the Bard. "Buy a boat and some nets and start to fish again. And take good care of my little girl." She was covering Ardra with kisses and tears, and telling her to be happy, to love, to have babies. "And remember, Ardra," she kept saying over and again, "always remember!"

Ardra didn't want to leave her mother all alone in the dark woods, but Boudicca was pushing the weeping girl away, urging her to mount the horse behind Finian.

"We can't leave her here," she heard the girl say to Finian as they rode away. "The wolves will come."

"Oh! I'm not afraid of any wolves!" Boudicca called after them, "wolves are cruel when they are hungry, but they're not cunning and greedy like the Strangers."

And that was the last thing Ardra ever heard her mother say.

***

The Strangers had fought dirty: very clever, admittedly, but dirty all the same. Nobody could doubt Queen Boudicca's courage, she who had left three of their cities blazing as red as her flame-coloured hair. But now it was her turn to feel the agony of defeat. And if it pleased the gods that she be conquered, she was brave enough to hasten her passage to the other world.

She was as hard as the land she sprang from, as courageous as the race of warriors she led: a tribe whom the Strangers never really tamed; who fought like lions and were proud and honest and brave right down to the last of them. Like her people, she feared nothing, except that the sky might fall in upon her. And Boudicca always knew what she had to do, so in the end it really was very simple: it was not for her to be paraded in chains in a Roman circus far beyond the ninth wave; not for her the comforts of a nice villa on the shores of the Tiber; not for her the patronage or mockery of her enemies.

Boudicca lay down in the chariot alongside Briana and felt in her belt for the phial of poison, made with the slim roots of hemlock. She drank it in one gulp and waited for its agonising clutches to take hold of her. While she waited, she put her strong white arm around Briana, resting the girl's head on her breast and recited to herself over and over:

I shall not be killed;
I shall not be hunted.
I shall not be captive;
I shall not be wounded.
Neither fire, nor sun, nor moon shall burn me.
Neither lake, nor river, nor sea shall drown me.

...until the time came when she no longer knew whether she was here or there. When the remnants of her tribe found their Queen deep in the forest the next day, she was as pale as the moon and she and her darling Briana were cloaked in their thick red hair.

Cold she lies
Beneath the burial stone.
All the blood she shed
Could not save her own.

EPILOGUE
Time-of-brightness
North Wales,
May, 140CE

Gwendoline's great-grandmother had reached the proper end of her tale. She sat on her little stool lost in thought, with a sad look on her tiny wizened face.

"It's late, child," she said. "Your mother will be wondering where you are; she'll be worried."

Gwendoline had been so lost in the past, she had forgotten all about the time. She hadn't even noticed how hungry she was, having eaten the last of the flat-cakes ages ago.

"But what happened to the Iceni?" she asked, in a voice much softened now from the angry one she had brought to the little round-house.

"Oh, the usual thing that happens after a great defeat. The Strangers tried to destroy everything that remained: the crops were all burnt to the ground; the cattle slaughtered; people's homes were put to the torch; the great fort at Venta Icenorum, where Boudicca was born and grew up, was demolished. I expect you were wondering about the treasure in the secret fort, weren't you? Everyone always wants to know about that," the old Bard sniffed dismissively. "Well, as far as I know it's still there, across the misty plains in the middle of the salt marshes."

Gwendoline shook her head. "No," she said simply. "I didn't mean any of that. Those are only things really. I don't want to know about things. I meant what happened to the people?"

Her great-grandmother smiled and nodded her old white head approvingly. "Good girl!" she said. "All these years and you're the only one wise enough to ask about the greatest treasure of all: the spirit of the Iceni! Well, that fled into the Pale Lands: the lands that lie between the grey above and the green beneath at the edge of the great sea."

Gwendoline peered across at the old woman, who was looking right back at her through the wisps of smoke, with her own grey eyes as wide as the great sea itself. "You mean here, don't you?" she said.

Her great-grandmother smiled.

Outside Gwendoline could hear her mother and father and Cadman calling for her across the fields.

"That was a fantastic story," cried Gwendoline, kissing the old woman. "I want to be a Bard just like you when I grow up. Will you teach me all the songs?"

Her great-grandmother smiled. "Oh, but you know I'm terribly old, and it takes twelve years to learn how to sing to the ancient stories of our people."

"Well then," said Gwendoline decisively, "we'd better get started first thing tomorrow! And you are absolutely forbidden to go to the other world until I am a woman and know the songs well enough to teach them to my daughters! And then their daughters can teach their daughters, and on and on, and then," Gwendoline tossed her red hair and her grey eyes shone with pride, "your mother will never be forgotten. Will she? Not as long as people remember!"

And with that Gwendoline went running off to find her parents and her brother, leaving Old Ardra the Bard sitting all alone by her cauldron, dreaming of the future.

QUIZ

After you've finished the book, test yourself and see how well you remember what you've read.

1. In deciding between Prasutagus or Antedios as King of the Iceni, the Druids:
   Held the first general election in the British Isles
   Arranged a contest to see who could burp the loudest
   Gave up and decreed that they should do a job-share

2. How did the Iceni celebrate the beginning of summer?
   By swimming naked across the thawing river
   By driving their cattle through bonfires
   By holding the first beach barbecue of the year

3. Boudicca's first daughter was called:
   Nigella
   Haroldina
   Briana

4. The young fisherman who informed Prasutagus of the Strangers' arrival was known for being:
   Good-looking
   Prone to diarrhoea
   An excellent swordsman

5. The region the Strangers landed in was known as:
   Strawberry Fields
   The Red Lands
   King Crimson's Territory

6. The Iceni celebrated the Feast of Samhain by eating:
   The Salmon of Wisdom
   The Egg of Courage
   The Sausage of Knowledge

7. After being defeated by the Strangers, Prince Caradoc:
   Retired to his holiday home on the Costa Brava
   Was given a villa on the shores of the Tiber
   Retrained as a human rights lawyer

8. What was the Iceni warriors' favourite hairstyle?
   Rock-hard plaits streaked with white lime
   Afros dyed blue with woad
   Back-combed mullets with party glitter

9. What did the Romans offer to build for the people of Icenia?
   Heated swimming pools
   The first railway in the world
   Straight roads

10. What did the Augury predict to Boudicca would occur in Icenia?
    Chickens without wings
    Woods without trees
    Butter without unsaturated fat

11. Who did the Romans use to build their fort at Camulodunum?
    Trinovanteans
    Whitevanmen
    Cardassians

12. Who replaced Aulus Plautius as Governor of Britannia?
    Pubic Omnibus Stadia
    Publius Ostorius Scapula
    Publicus Octopus Spatula

13. What did the new Roman Governor forbid British natives from doing?
    Sleeping on their stomachs
    Riding horses without a licence
    Carrying weapons

14. How did Antedios die?
    He was boiled alive
    He choked on a pretzel
    He was assassinated by a crazy bard

15. When Prasutagus saw that the Iceni warriors were getting fat and lazy he:
    Put them on the Atkins diet
    Made them go swimming every afternoon
    Cancelled the sports channel satellite TV subscription

16. What did the Druids use to tell the future?
    A pack of cards
    A barometer and a compass
    The knuckle bones of a pig

17. Boudicca's younger daughter Ardra enjoyed:
    Playing her harp and singing
    Painting her hair and nails
    Practising her sword skills with her friends

18. What did the Iceni traditionally do when someone died?
   Cry
   Laugh
   Make flatbread

19. How did Boudicca try to scare the people of Camulodunum?
   By putting up subversive graffiti throughout the city overnight
   By hiding behind a column and sticking her tongue out at people who passed
   By toppling a statue of Victory in the city

20. What animal was used to predict the outcome of Boudicca's final battle?
   An elephant
   A hare
   A Shetland pony

Dear Reader,

The problem with writing a book about Boudicca is that there is very little reliable information about her. The only account we have of Boudicca and her Rebellion that was written close to the event (what historians call a "Primary Source"), is that given by the historian Tacitus in his Annals. (You can find the relevant section on this website: http://www.gallica.co.uk/celts/boudica.htm) But beware! This is history as recorded by the Victors – those rascally Romans. The Celts, you see, were not all that good at writing things down and poor old Boudicca was pretty much forgotten until the nineteenth century... If you do read Tacitus's account, bear in mind that he never clapped eyes on Boudicca and didn't write his Annals until about forty or fifty years after Boudicca's last great battle. The only other near-contemporary account we have was written by a Greek historian called Dio Cassius. He gives us the description of Boudicca as a large, stroppy red-head, and his version is much more gory than Tacitus's, but he was writing about 150 years later.

So, if you want to know more about Boudicca, you'll have to do what I did: use your imagination, and read some books that tell you as much as historians know about the times in which she lived. Here are some titles I would recommend if you are serious about finding out more:

Tony CONRAN (transl): Welsh Verse (Seren, 2003) (Some of these are quite difficult, and written much later than Boudicca's time, but they give you an impression of the Celtic people).
Miranda Jane GREEN: Celtic Myths (British Museum Press, 1993)
Jenny HALL & Christine JONES: Roman Britain (BBC Educational Publishing, 1993) This is a good book for kids. The others are "proper" histories.

Caitlin MATTHEWS: The Celtic Tradition (Element Books, 1989)
I.A. RICHMOND: Roman Britain (Pelican History of England, 1975)
W.F. & N.G. RITCHIE: Celtic Warriors (Shire Archaeology, 1997)
Ward RUTHERFORD: Celtic Mythology (Aquarian Press, 1987)

I also recommend the following web-sites:

http://www.bgfl.org/bgfl/custom/resources_ftp/client_ftp/ks2/history/boudicca/index.htm This is a good site for younger children who like their history simple.

The Great North Museum http://museums.ncl.ac.uk/ has a very good section on Roman Britain. Highly recommended for 7-11 year olds

The Channel Four web-site has a very informative and detailed account of Boudicca's story: http://www.channel4.com/history/microsites/H/history/a-b/boud.html

http://www.stephen.j.murray.btinternet.co.uk/tribesv7.htm a good introductory site on the British tribes at the Time of the Roman Invasion

The British Museum Web-site has a good section on the Druids: http://www.thebritishmuseum.ac.uk/

http://www.roman-britain.org/tribes.htm is a fantastic site on the Celtic Tribes. It is highly recommended and full of information, though it's not specifically designed for children.

Happy reading!!

Siân Busby,
London, January 2006

AUTHOR BIOGRAPHY

Siân Busby is the author of the highly acclaimed *A Wonderful Little Girl* (2003) and *The Cruel Mother,* which won Mind Book of the Year 2005 (Short Books). She is also a film-maker, scriptwriter and digital artist. She lives in London with her husband and two sons.